U316 Book 1

ENVIRONMENTAL CHANGES: GLOBAL CHALLENGES

edited by
Mark Brandon and Nigel Clark

THE ENVIRONMENTAL WEB  U316

Cover images courtesy of Mark Brandon. From left to right: lenticular clouds over Anvers Island, Antarctic Peninsula; a chinstrap penguin chick on its nest high above the Southern Ocean; a mountain at the entrance to the Lemaire Channel on the Antarctic Peninsula; part of a sledging food cache from 1962.

This publication forms part of an Open University course U316 *The Environmental Web*. The complete list of texts which make up this course can be found on the back cover. Details of this and other Open University courses can be obtained from the Course Information and Advice Centre, PO Box 724, The Open University, Milton Keynes MK7 6ZS, United Kingdom: tel. +44 (0)1908 653231, e-mail general enquiries@open.ac.uk

Alternatively, you may visit the Open University website at http://www.open.ac.uk where you can learn more about the wide range of courses and packs offered at all levels by The Open University.

To purchase a selection of Open University course materials visit the webshop at www.ouw.co.uk, or, contact Open University Worldwide, Michael Young Building, Walton Hall, Milton Keynes MK7 6AA, United Kingdom for a brochure: tel. +44 (0)1908 858785; fax +44 (0)1908 858787; e-mail ouwenq@open.ac.uk

The Open University
Walton Hall, Milton Keynes
MK7 6AA

First published 2003

Copyright © 2003 The Open University

All rights reserved. No part of this publication may be reproduced, stored in a retrieval system, transmitted or utilized in any form or by any means, electronic, mechanical, photocopying, recording or otherwise, without written permission from the publisher or a licence from the Copyright Licensing Agency Ltd. Details of such licences (for reprographic reproduction) may be obtained from the Copyright Licensing Agency Ltd of 90 Tottenham Court Road, London W1T 4LP.

Edited, designed and typeset by The Open University.

Printed and bound in the United Kingdom by The Bath Press, Glasgow.

ISBN 0 7492 56788

1.1

u316 book 1i1.1

U316 *The Environmental Web* Course Team

Course Team Chair

Jonathan Silvertown, Department of Biological Sciences, Faculty of Science

Course Managers

Tracy Finnegan, Department of Biological Sciences, Faculty of Science
Marion Hall, Department of Biological Sciences, Faculty of Science

Course Team Assistant

Catherine Eden, Department of Biological Sciences, Faculty of Science

Open University Authors

Mark Brandon, Department of Earth Sciences, Faculty of Science
(Chair and author Block 1)
Nigel Clark, Department of Geography, Faculty of Social Science (Block 1)
Mike Dodd, Department of Biological Sciences, Faculty of Science (Block 2)
Marion Hall, Department of Biological Sciences, Faculty of Science (Block 1)
Stephen Peake, Department of Design and Innovation, Faculty of Technology
(Co-Chair and author Block 3)
Irene Ridge, Department of Biological Sciences, Faculty of Science (Block 2)
Jonathan Silvertown, Department of Biological Sciences, Faculty of Science
(Chair and author Block 2)
Sandrine Simon, Systems Department, Faculty of Technology
(Chair and author Block 4)
Joe Smith, Department of Geography, Faculty of Social Science (Co-Chair and author Block 3)

Software Development

Phil Butcher, Learning and Teaching Solutions (CD-ROM development)
Sophia Braybrooke, Learning and Teaching Solutions (CD-ROM development)
Andrea Goodinson, Learning and Teaching Solutions (Web development)
Jason Jarratt, Learning and Teaching Solutions (CD-ROM development)
Ross Mackenzie, Learning and Teaching Solutions (Web development)
Gloria Medina, Faculty of Science (Software Production Manager and academic liaison)
Trent Williams, Learning and Teaching Solutions (Web development)
Damion Young, Learning and Teaching Solutions (CD-ROM and Web development)

Editors

Sheila Dunleavy
Ian Nuttall
Bina Sharma
Dick Sharp

Graphic Design

Sue Dobson
Carl Gibbard
David Winter

BBC/OU Production Centre

Sue Nuttall (Video for CD-ROM)

Other Contributors

Gary Alexander, Department of Telematics, Faculty of Technology (Block 4)
John Baxter, Faculty of Science (Community Interactions)
Roger Blackmore, Faculty of Technology (Day School, Project, activities for Block 1)
Gloria Medina (activities for Blocks 1 and 4)
Richard Treves, Faculty of Technology (Block 1)

Consultants

Claire Appleby, Open University Associate Lecturer (Block 4)
Hilary Denny, Open University Associate Lecturer
(Associate Lecturer recruitment, training and support)
Sarah Hardy (ECA)
Alex Kirby, BBC News Online environment correspondent (activities for Block 3)
Bob MacQueen, Open University Associate Lecturer (Reader)
Steve Millar, Open University Associate Lecturer (Reader)
Donal O'Donnell, Open University Associate Lecturer (Reader)
Julian Priddle, Science Teaching and Education Partnership (Block 1)

External Assessors

Professor Sandy Crosbie, Faculty of Science and Engineering,
University of Edinburgh (Course Assessor)
Dr Christopher Hope, Judge Institute of Management Studies, University of Cambridge (Block 3)
Dr John Shears, British Antarctic Survey, Cambridge (Block 1)
Mr David Streeter, School of Biological Sciences, University of Sussex (Block 2)
Dr Caroline Sullivan, Centre for Ecology and Hydrology at Wallingford, Oxfordshire (Block 4)

Contents

1 Shrinking worlds: islands and environmental change

Prepared for the course team by Nigel Clark

1.1 Introducing *The Environmental Web*

Over recent decades people and places around the world have been drawn into closer contact. We are getting used to the idea that money, goods, people and ideas flow around the planet with a speed and intensity that would have been surprising even 50 years ago. Many of us are also becoming aware that there is a price to pay for this relentless activity, a cost that must be borne by the life-support systems of the Earth. Initially appearing as an unfortunate side effect of our way of life, environmental problems now loom large in the way we perceive and experience the world. No sooner had we begun to conceive of our planet as a 'whole' — a single, interconnected system — than it became apparent that this system was under duress — stirred, shaken and disturbed by our human interventions. Today, environmental problems and 'global' consciousness have become inseparable.

Sooner or later, most environmental problems flow over the bounds of our neighbourhoods, our counties or even our countries. Some are fully global in both cause and effect. The possibility that human activities are collectively transforming the climate of the entire planet must surely be one of the most perturbing messages that humankind has ever had to confront. Quite suddenly, it seems, we are having to grapple with the knowledge that emissions from the energy we consume in our work and play directly impact on people and other living things on the far side of the planet — and will continue to do so long after we are gone. In a less direct way, through the workings of the global economy, many of the things we do have repercussions elsewhere in the world. The materials we work with, the things we buy and the investments we make affect people and their environments half a world away.

Viewed in this way, the scale and complexity of environmental issues can seem overwhelming, as if to thwart and belittle any intention we have to take positive action. But the pathways and connections that weave all of us into the wider world can do more than simply submit us to forces beyond our control. Many of the ties that bind us into the global economy can also bring us into contact with other people, who share our feelings and concerns, and they can give us access to information and tools that can help us turn our intentions into actions. Over the same decades that the world seems to have shrunk and its environmental problems grown, people have begun to cooperate in new ways — locally, nationally, and across the planet. Some of these new modes of meeting and making decisions involve government officials and scientific experts. But other new forms of communication and cooperative action involve groups of ordinary individuals, people whose experiences, insights and ideas seem to form a more 'everyday' world. Today, there is a growing feeling that ordinary people working together can, and should, make a difference to the way that global problems are dealt with and to the way the world is run.

This course, *The Environmental Web*, is about understanding and looking after the life-forms and land-forms we depend upon. It is about getting a handle on, and responding to, the environmental challenges we face, from our backyard to the entire globe. And it is about making sense of connections that bind the local and global, in order that we might make these linkages work for us and for the sort of world we want to live in. As you may have guessed, the title *The Environmental Web* conjures up different sorts of interconnectivity. It refers to ecological 'webs' — the weave of living things, cycles of matter and flows of energy that make up the natural world. It also refers to the networks and exchanges that our own species have added to the world: the patterns of connectivity that make up our social realm.

Defining what is meant by 'nature' or 'the natural world' and what is meant by 'society' or the social world has never been easy, and it is getting harder all the time. In this course, we take 'society' or 'the social' as referring to all those processes and things that human agency has brought into the world, and 'nature' or 'the natural' as referring to these forms and process that have came into existence prior to, or independently from human agency. In this sense, all human social achievements are ultimately reliant on natural processes or resources. At the same time, the more that social agency transforms the world, the more difficult it becomes to identify or describe a 'nature' that is distinct from 'society'.

In *The Environmental Web*, we deal with the entanglement of the natural and the social by treating nature and society as different, but interrelated systems. By a **system** we mean any group of parts or components that interact with each other, in such a way that any change made to one part will affect at least some of the other parts. Some systems, like a family of human beings or the Solar System have a small number of 'components'. But most of the systems we will be dealing with — such as ecosystems, climate systems and social systems — have many parts (Figure 1.1a, b).

- Can you think of three other systems you have dealings with in your everyday life?

- There are many possible answers. You may have given an example of an institution like a workplace or school. These come under the category of social systems. You may have thought of technological systems, such as gadgets or machines. Or you may have thought of a physical system, such as your own body.

Thinking about systems makes it easier to come and go from the natural world to the social world, and to move between different scales — from the microscopic to the global — without losing our bearings. Rather than thinking about nature and society as separate spheres, they are conceived of as interlinked systems, at least partially open to each other and in constant exchange.

(a)

(b)

Figure 1.1 Two examples of systems with many parts: (a) an aerial view of a 'spaghetti junction' road network; (b) a braided river in Siberia.

Thinking in terms of 'systems' focuses attention on connections between parts or individuals or groups, and helps us to recognize that relationships are as important as the parts themselves. Over recent decades, new information and communication technologies (ICTs) have helped bring this lesson home — by giving increasing numbers of people the chance to experience a form of interconnectivity that is unprecedented in its capacity to bring distant people and places into conversation. Our title, *The Environmental Web*, alludes to these new modes of electronic connectivity, their impact on the world, and their potential for engaging with environmental issues in novel ways.

While other means of communicating, such as print, TV broadcasting and face-to-face encounters lose none of their importance, new technologies have a capacity to combine the advantages of other media. By linking computers, phones and databases into a global network, the Internet allows us to search and retrieve stored information, and to share our knowledge, thoughts and experiences with like-minded people wherever they are in the world. ICTs can help us respond to environmental problems on the same terrain they present themselves. That is, if the problems we are facing link the local with the global in dense and complicated ways, then we must make the most of tools that enable our learning and action to likewise form far-reaching interconnections, bridging the local and global.

'The Internet', as one activist put it, 'has become the latest, greatest arrow in our quiver of social activism' (cited in French, 2000, p. 163). What greatly appeals to many Internet users is that no single group or organization controls the content or the development of the new networks. For many people, this adds to the feeling that their own participation in ICT-mediated exchanges is part of a turn towards popular or 'grassroots' involvement in important events.

1.2 Connected planet, divided world

The term frequently used to capture all the process that are bringing different parts of the globe into closer connection, and to convey the experience of the planet as a single place is **globalization**. Environmental problems are part of the process of globalization, but at the same time, other forms of global interconnectivity play an important role in the way people experience and respond to environmental issues. Globalization is the first of the four key themes or concepts that run through this course. The others, which we will introduce you to over the next two chapters, are sustainability, uncertainty and governance. These are terms that are used frequently in the arena of environmental thought and action: each offers a handle on an important aspect of environmental problems and problem solving. But at the same time, they also direct our attention to major fault-lines in environmental thought and practice — to the points that are most debated and contested.

One of the tensions that run through the concept of globalization is that it conjures a sense of unity and oneness, but at the same time, it has to encompass deep divisions. In thinking of the planet as an interconnected whole, there is a temptation to think of everyone as 'being in the same boat'. But, as much as they draw us together, environmental problems and other forms of global interconnectedness are played out in a very uneven world. Some people are more vulnerable to environmental threats and disasters than others. And those most at risk often have the least access to the resources and tools that could make their lives safer and easier. Just as we tend to speak of the 'whole earth' and the 'endangered earth' in the same breath, so too have global environmental issues and worldwide inequity become deeply entangled.

There are several terms in common usage as shorthand for these divides: the 'First' and the 'Third' Worlds, the 'North' and the 'South', the 'developed' and the 'underdeveloped' world, the 'west' and the rest. None of these terms captures the complications and nuances of global inequality, yet each conveys something of the vast imbalances in wealth, power and opportunity that rend social life at many levels across the planet (Figures 1.2, 1.3).

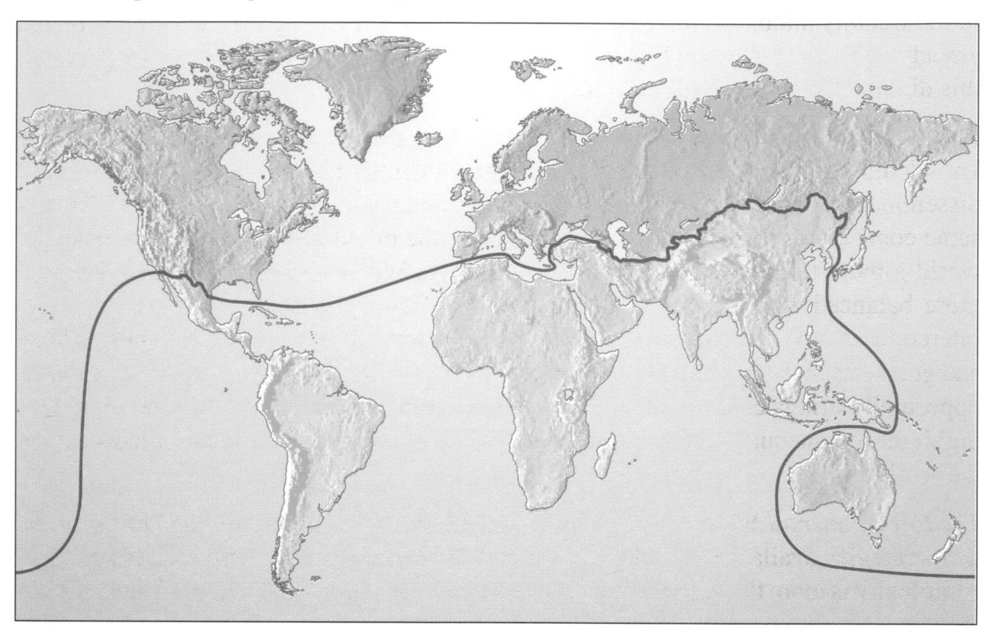

Figure 1.2 This figure shows how the Independent Commission on International Development Issues divided the world in 1980. This division between a rich 'North' and a poor 'South' is now seen as over-simplistic and outdated.

Figure 1.3 Suzhou Creek, Shanghai, a place where the 'developed' and the 'underdeveloped' worlds overlap.

The collision between issues of environmental degradation and questions of global inequality is one of the greatest challenges faced by the contemporary world. Put simply, the problem is this: the message from environmentalists is that current levels of global industrial activity are having serious long-term impacts on the planet. However, the benefits of industrial development have been unevenly distributed, favouring the wealthier 'developed' countries. Many of those who speak for the less-developed world have been making strong claims that the benefits from the exploitation of the planet's resources should not be restricted to a minority of the world's population. Unfortunately, should all or even most of the rest of the world attain the level of material consumption of the wealthy minority (which itself shows no sign of levelling off), the strains on the already stressed planet will be vastly increased. Though not always in the foreground, this dilemma is a central part of the framework of this course.

Ideally, new forms of communication should help people all around the world share knowledge and experiences about the predicaments they are in. Moreover, rapid dissemination of news of dangers and disasters could help the most vulnerable. But the same connections that might help us respond to the plight of others can also make the world a more turbulent and uncontrollable place. Whatever form our ideals about a more balanced world might take, there is little doubt that new forms of electronic interconnectivity make it harder to regulate the flow of information, images, money and goods around the planet. In a world that is subject to such rapid change, every new opportunity brings costs and risks. Today, we might also speak of a 'digital divide' to highlight the unequal access to information and communication technologies across the world.

The Environmental Web takes a global focus on environmental issues and on the tools and strategies available to address these issues. However, the whole planet in all its complexity is more than anyone can handle. This course ventures into the global terrain in stages, beginning in this book with two examples: small oceanic islands and the continent of Antarctica. These may seem like exotic locations, and you may be wondering why we don't start closer to home. What we hope you will recognize, quite early on, is that home and far away are linked in some quite extraordinary ways, and that nowhere is too distant or different to have profound relevance for our own locales — and of course vice versa. Environmental thought and action is a kind of journeying, and these journeys call for some quite imaginative leaps in space and, moreover, in time, as we shall see later.

Oceanic islands are an excellent starting point because of their extreme vulnerability to certain sorts of global environmental change. But these islands are not simply vulnerable places. Their human and non-human inhabitants are far more than victims-in-waiting. Through studying islands, we can also learn about the creative forces in both the natural and social realms. Although small oceanic islands may at first seem a world away, they can teach us about what happens on larger islands such as the British Isles or even on continents.

Antarctica might seem like an odd introduction to environmental issues, given that it has no indigenous human population. What could we learn about the relationship between humans and nature in a place that seems to have so much of the latter and so few of the former? But the fact that Antarctica — along with the frigid Southern Ocean that surrounds it — falls outside the jurisdiction of any one nation makes it a very interesting case study for the way that humankind deals with the places we have in common. At one time, the seas, islands and coastlines of Antarctica were the site of some of the most extreme over-exploitation by humans of natural resources the planet has witnessed. But on a more positive note, as you will see, Antarctica (Figure 1.4, overleaf) and the Southern Ocean show the way humankind can collectively protect its shared or common spaces.

Figure 1.4 The Antarctic Peninsula.

Working through the island example you will encounter a number of interrelated environmental problems. You will be returning to each of these problems and the questions they raise in greater depth later in the course. Along the way, we will introduce you to (or remind you about) some of the skills and techniques for tracking down information that you will need for the course. By the end of this book you should have a feel for the severity and complexity of environmental problems, and you will have had a taste of the interdisciplinary approach that defines this course.

Figure 1.5 The idyllic vision of a tropical island.

1.3 Troubled waters: the predicament of islands

So let's get our feet wet. How does the idea of suddenly being transported to a tropical island sound? If all your responsibilities were taken care of, how would you feel about being whisked away right now — if just for a while? What ideas and images go through your mind when you think about tropical islands? If you live under the grey skies of Northern Europe it's quite likely that sunshine and sandy beaches come to mind (Figure 1.5). But is there more to it than this? If travel literature and tourist brochures are anything to go by, then much of the attraction of islands is about 'getting away from it all' — putting your feet up, and putting some distance between yourself and your busy, everyday life.

There seems to be something about crossing an ocean, about landing somewhere separated by a good stretch of sea from where you live and your normal life, that has a deep appeal. This appeal seems to apply no less to people in the British Isles, which of course are large islands themselves. The further from home you go, the more chance there is that your island experience, or your island imagining is coloured by ideas of going somewhere 'unspoilt', a place somehow made remote by water and by distance from the woes and cares of civilization.

This is how a resort in the Maldives, a cluster of islands in the Indian Ocean, appeals to the 'island imagination' on their website:

> Imagine an undisturbed lush green tropical forest. Exotic tropical blooms and ripe luscious fruits. The music of birds calling out to each other. The gentle sound of wind rustling the leaves. The rushing of waves to shore in the background — the perfect tropical symphony. What would you call a place such as this? Eden? We call it Palm Beach Island.

(Palm Beach, Maldives, 1997)

It's hard to deny the appeal, especially when it's raining and life's responsibilities are pressing. But 'Eden' is a tricky thing to pull off, even if you have a tropical island at your disposal. If you've ever visited a beach resort that plays on beautiful scenery and 'getting away from it all', or if you've heard tales from people who have, you may have a feeling for the fine line any such attraction treads. A tourist resort is there to make money, and generally, the more tourists and the more facilities to accommodate tourists, the more money gets made. Hence the 'holiday in hell' stories — when the 'idyllic' beachfront hotel turns out to be next to a building site, clattering with activity from dawn till dusk (Figure 1.6). Every developer knows the risk: not enough development and moneymaking opportunities are lost. Too much and the charm that attracted visitors could be lost forever.

Figure 1.6 Tourist development — or overdevelopment?

As someone with an interest in the environment, you will probably be aware that this 'development' is about more than selling charm or preserving scenery. It is about balancing facilities with demands on resources. More visitors and more infrastructure means mounting pressure on the environment and all the services it provides. This is the tension between development and preserving the environment, and on a small island with limited space this tension can be extreme.

Let's hear more about these dilemmas by visiting the Maldives, the islands that include the Palm Beach resort that was selling its charms a few paragraphs ago. The following readings and activity are an essential part of this chapter, and will provide you with a grounding for thinking about the link between development and the environment.

Read the newspaper articles about the Maldives, 'A thousand isles from nowhere', followed by 'Climate change will endanger low-lying island states' available in the Offprints. Newspapers date quickly, but the issues raised in the readings are likely to be with us for the forseeable future. As you are reading, think about the tension between tourist development and preserving the environment that both writers refer to and take note of the way these issues are being addressed in the Maldives.

Activity 1.1 The view from the Maldives

Now consider your first reactions to these articles. Think back to your response to the earlier prompt about imagining a quick getaway to a balmy, unspoilt tropical island. Have these accounts of the Maldives changed the way you think about tropical islands? Or were you already familiar with global climate change? As we proceed, we will be looking into the issues raised in these articles in more depth, but for the moment just jot down your initial feelings.

For example:

- How would you feel about living with the uncertainty about the future that the Maldivians face?
- Do you feel a connection between where you live and the way you live, and the predicament of the Maldivians?

Comment

One reaction might be a feeling of sympathy for the Maldivians. Perhaps you also felt concern for your own situation, a creeping sense that the risks and uncertainties experienced by people on small oceanic islands might one day be facing you. Did you wonder about the impact of your life-style and how this contributes —

negatively or positively — to the lives of people elsewhere? You might have recalled that the fantasy of 'getting away from it all' has a lot to do with escaping your normal, everyday responsibilities. Perhaps the plight of small island people suggested another sort of 'responsibility': whether people in one part of the world can be held responsible for the plight of others in distant places.

Another reaction to these articles could be a desire to be better informed. There are strong claims being made, but also some considerable uncertainties about the future of low-lying islands like the Maldives. Your response may well have been to wish for more evidence about what is happening to the environment and about what is likely to happen in the future. These are ideas we will return to later in this chapter.

1.3.1 When sustainability met development

For the moment, let's set aside the question of global climate change, and focus on the way the Maldivians are dealing with the development of their tourist industry and its environmental implications. The two newspaper articles you read were written by journalists from different countries — one British, the other from the Maldives — and they seem to have dissimilar intentions and different audiences in mind. Nevertheless, they agree that the Maldivians are taking the relationship between tourist development and environmental protection very seriously (Figure 1.7).

Figure 1.7 A Maldives tourist resort designed and built in line with environmental guidelines.

- Can you recall five ways in which the Maldivians are attempting to minimize the environmental impacts of tourism?

- 1 They limit tourist development to certain islands.

  2 On these islands development is restricted to 20% of the total surface area.

3 There are limits on the height of buildings (the height of a mature palm tree).

4 There are restrictions on the removal of vegetation and on damage to the marine environment.

5 There are strict standards for managing water and waste.

Clearly, the Maldivians are counting on their tourist industry for revenue, and therefore to assist **development**. By development, we mean the attainment of chosen social and economic goals by a social group (in this context a country). The Maldivians are taking measures to ensure that the growth of the tourist industry does not undermine the environmental resources or scenic attractions that are their draw-card. Reading between the lines, it also seems that this careful management of the tourist industry is also intended to protect the culture of the islands — especially the Islamic way of life — from foreign influences.

- What term did President Gayoom use to describe the tourist development strategy in the Maldives?

- Sustainability.

Sustainability is the second of our four key course themes. By sustainability what is meant is the capacity to live without undermining the systems that support life. Not surprisingly, this has emerged as one of the central issues of contemporary environmentalism. One way of framing the sustainability issue is to ask whether we can leave our children, grandchildren or generations further down the line with an environment of the same quality, or better, than our own.

The link between sustainability and development sounds straightforward. Development that does not undermine its own foundations is more desirable than development that destroys the environmental or cultural resources it relies upon. Today, sustainable development dominates discussions of the global environmental predicament, but it is more complex and contested than it first appears. Where sustainability alludes primarily to concerns about long-term environmental degradation, development refers to the issue of the differences in wealth and power that divide the world's nations — and the need to address this gap. Linking these two themes together requires an explicit connection between the environmental issues and global economic inequality. This connection has not always been obvious or apparent, and you should be mindful that not everyone is happy with the way the link has been forged.

When environmental concerns were raised in the 1960s, most attention was fixed on conditions in the wealthiest and most developed countries, or on single environmental issues such as pollution or saving the great whales. It was in these countries that the negative impacts of industry and industrialized agriculture and fishing seemed most apparent. Many of the pioneer environmentalists of the 1960s and 1970s argued that the ever-increasing economic growth that everyone seemed to take for granted must eventually come up against the limits of a finite planet. The conclusion usually drawn from this observation was that the notion of 'progress' based on limitless growth — an idea at the heart of modern western civilization was due for a complete overhaul.

This was not a popular message for most governments or for the international business community — who clearly saw their interests lying in further economic growth.

The idea of absolute limits to growth was particularly unappealing to leaders of the 'South' or the 'less-developed world' who saw it as a threat to their aspirations to bring their own economies to the level of the wealthier countries. This issue came up at the 1972 United Nations Conference on the Human Environment held in Stockholm: environmentalism's full debut on the international political stage. Less-developed countries were reassured by the rest of the world community that the 'no-growth' option would not be seriously considered. Stockholm gave rise to the first formal declaration that development and environmental concern were expected to go hand in hand. It was, however, a rather brief and vague pronouncement.

It was over a decade later that the union between sustainability and development was fully cemented. The World Commission on Environment and Development (WCED), set up by the United Nations in 1983, brought the notion of **sustainable development** into prominence. Sustainable development emerged as catchphrase for a qualitatively new sort of economic growth that would minimize human impacts on the environment and greatly improve the living standards of the majority of the world's people. The WCED's official report *Our Common Future* gave a definition that remains influential:

> Sustainable development seeks to meet the needs and aspirations of the present without compromising the ability to meet those of the future. Far from requiring the cessation of economic growth, it recognizes that the problems of poverty and underdevelopment cannot be solved unless we have a new era of growth in which developing countries play a large role and reap large benefits... policymakers guided by the concept of sustainable development will necessarily work to assure that growing economies remain firmly attached to their ecological roots and that these roots are protected. Environmental protection is thus inherent in the concept of sustainable development...
>
> (WCED, 1987, p. 40)

The idea of sustainable development now has a hold on the imagination of many environmentally aware people worldwide. The sensible and proactive way that the Maldivians are managing their tourist industry is one of many attempts to put the idea into practice. But arguably, the dilemma that brought sustainability and development together has never disappeared. The concept has been further explored, pulled apart, redefined and even accused of being a contradiction in terms! To see what is at stake, let's return to our two articles on the Maldives.

1.3.2 Sustainability and global environmental change

You will need no reminding that the environmental issue that most worries the Maldivians is changes in the Earth's climate. Both the articles you read earlier refer to arguments that human activities are contributing to an overall warming of the planet. Human interventions may well have had impacts on climate in the past, but never before has there been such widespread and popular awareness about this phenomenon. Clearly, your perceptions of the current situation depend on where in the world you are living — and global climate change may not initially strike you as a 'problem' at all. It is worth pausing and trying to remember the first time you heard about 'global warming'. Was it frightening? Or was there at least some appeal in the idea?

For example, the BBC provides a hands-on kit for children, called the *Weather Activity Set*, to encourage children to learn about local and global weather. It says:

> By the middle of the 21st century, the British Isles could have a more Mediterranean climate. Most of our rain will fall in milder and shorter winters, and we will have longer, drier, warmer summers. Such changes in our weather pattern will inevitably lead to life-style changes.
>
> (Giles and Mortimer, 1998, p. 31)

These life-style changes are illustrated by someone on a deck chair, sipping a drink!

Living on a low-lying island gives a rather different perspective on climate change.

From the newspaper articles, can you recall four problems related to climate change that are facing the Maldives?

1. An increase in extreme weather events — including storm surges.
2. Coastal erosion, possibly even total inundation of islands.
3. Saltwater contamination of ground freshwater supplies (aquifers).
4. Damage to coral reefs and general, widespread disturbance of marine ecosystems.

For all their efforts at the local level, the Maldivians are extremely vulnerable to global environmental changes that they can do little about (Figure 1.8). These changes could not only undo their own efforts at sustainable development, but completely destroy their own environment. We will return to the issue of climate change in more depth in Book 3, but for now it is enough to say that it is overall energy use across the planet that determines the human contribution to climate change. In this regard, the Maldivians' contribution to global energy use is tiny, and therefore out of all proportion to the costs they appear to be facing.

Figure 1.8 A tropical island during a cyclone.

The dilemma of the Maldivians highlights the tension that gave rise to the concept of sustainable development in the first place. At the same time, however, it points to the tensions that remain unresolved. When the World Commission on Environment and Development was attempting to reconcile development and sustainability, global climate change was already on the agenda. The WCED was aware that consuming fossil fuels, as well as cutting and burning forests, was resulting in a build-up of carbon dioxide in the Earth's atmosphere, which would trap solar radiation and result in global warming. *Our Common Future* raised the prospect of climatic change upsetting global agricultural production, together with sea-level rises devastating low-lying areas — and all within the next half-century. Clearly the patterns of energy use that had played such an important part in the economic growth of the most developed countries could not be replicated in the less-developed countries without dire environmental consequences.

But as you saw above, representatives of the less-developed world presented a case that the benefits accruing from the exploitation of global resources should be for all. This was taken to mean that less-developed countries had a right to pursue the pattern of economic development that had worked for the developed economies. At the same time, it was becoming apparent that many of the places likely to suffer the most from climate change, such as river deltas, and low-lying islands and atolls, were in the less-developed world. As in the case of the Maldives, this meant that people who had not yet made a large contribution to global energy use, or shared most of its benefits were likely to suffer most from the negative impacts of economic growth.

The WCED calculated the increase in industrial output that would be necessary to raise the production and consumption levels of the less-developed world to those of the developed world. Assuming — or rather, hoping — that world population would stop growing in the 21st century, it concluded that a *five- to tenfold* increase in the existing global industrial outputs would be required (WCED, 1987, p. 15). And remember, this was the prognosis of environmentally aware advisors and experts, not sceptics of environmental change. Taking into account that 1980s levels of production were below those of today, it is worth stopping and thinking about the environmental implications of multiplying overall global energy use and raw material consumption (along with all the associated emissions and waste products) by even the lower estimate of fivefold.

Don't worry about calculations, just consider whether the world that might result would provide future generations with the same or better environmental conditions than we experience today. Keep this in mind when you encounter the idea of sustainable development.

Despite their clear preference for an alternative to the 'limits-to-growth' idea, the WCED could not entirely evade the message of earlier environmentalists that the Earth was essentially finite. As its report conceded:

> The ultimate limits to global development are perhaps determined by the availability of energy resources and the biosphere's capacity to absorb the by-products of energy use.
>
> (WCED, 1987, p. 58)

As sketched out in *Our Common Future*, sustainable development was an attempt to imagine a way out of this bind. Economic growth would proceed, but it would be uncoupled from the excessive use of non-renewable energy and materials. The proposals offered hinged mostly on increasing the efficiency of production, in particular replacing non-renewable fuels with renewable energy sources that do not contribute to global warming. This is discussed in depth in Book 3. What is important at this stage is that you gain a sense of the immensity of the dilemma that 'fuelled' the idea of sustainable development. This understanding is vital if we are to consider where we stand with this quandary today.

You should now go to the Web to do the activities associated with Chapter 1.

1.3.3 The ongoing challenge of sustainability

The Maldives may be exceptional in their vulnerability to environmental change, but what does their predicament tell us about the tension between development and sustainability? It is still early days to be pondering problems of this complexity, but the situation prompts a number of ideas and questions.

Perhaps the most obvious response is that the tensions between sustainability and development are as acute today as when the WCED wrote its report in the 1980s. The climate change issue has grown, and yet there still seems to be faith in the idea that development can, and should continue. Tension appears to be strongest between the local level — over which the Maldivians have some degree of influence or control — and the global level — where the Maldivians have little or no control. The problem, as you may have noted, is that these global changes have profound local effects.

What sort of questions does this conflict raise? There appear to be many unknowns about issues that threaten the Maldivians and others in low-lying areas. Will sea-level rise? If so, by how much and how fast? Are the observed changes due to human impacts — or other causes? If dramatic changes are going occur over the next century, what are the implications for the Maldives and other vulnerable low-lying coastal areas? If those of us who have benefited from intensive energy use are in some sense responsible for global environmental changes, what demands might the Maldivians make of us? And what kinds of response could we make?

It is useful to see how a simple-sounding dilemma quickly gives rise to a cascade of questions. These are the types of question we will pose throughout the course, and we will be offering you the kind of resources and skills you need to set about addressing them. We also hope to stimulate your curiosity and to encourage you to formulate your own questions! Note that we have not talked about 'solving' environmental problems. We don't mean they are insoluble, but the issues *are* complex and tangled. All our actions are likely to have unforeseen as well as anticipated consequences. Solutions have a way of generating new problems, just as some problems can have surprising benefits, when viewed from a different perspective.

Now we will look more closely at the environmental changes that haunt both the articles on the Maldives. We start by asking what we need to know in order to assess the claims being made about global warming and sea-level change. What sort of information do we need in order to make decisions and take effective action? Who has the knowledge or the information we require? Are all the data we need available? And what happens when information sources or knowledge claims turn out to be conflicting?

1.4 Global environmental change: substantiating the charges

Human fear of world-threatening cataclysms such as great floods have a long and colourful history. What sets contemporary environmental concerns apart is an insistence on evidence to back up claims and predictions. When we think of ourselves as 'modern', a large part of this self-definition rests on the fact that we now make recourse to science rather than other kinds of stories — such as myths or religion — to explain the way our world works. The modern trust in science hinges on the procedures through which knowledge claims are made and evaluated, rather than on the personal authority of whoever voiced the claims. When the President of the Maldives makes a statement to the global community, it is not surprising to see that he backs up his claim with reference to scientific evidence. As he announced in the newspaper article, 'The IPCC has established that human activities are changing the world's climate system'. But who is the IPCC? On what grounds can it claim knowledge about the trends in climate of the entire Earth?

It may seem obvious that scientific evidence is needed to assess a claim about an environmental problem, or at least to give this assessment legitimacy. However, it has not always been this straightforward. In the 1960s and 70s many environmentalists viewed the achievements of science as being heavily implicated in the 'environmental crisis' — and there were appeals for the rejection of the so-called 'scientific worldview'. There is much to be said for this critique of applied science, and many environmentalists remain deeply sceptical of the uses to which scientific knowledge has been put. At the same time, we should be mindful that the modern environmental movement is highly dependent on scientific evidence to substantiate its claims. Moreover, in many, if not the majority of cases, it has been concerned scientists who have played a pivotal role in bringing environmental issues to public attention. In the 1980s, as concern over the environment crystallized into the concept of 'global environmental change', voices calling for the wholehearted rejection of scientific values faded into the margins of environmental thought and practice.

Figure 1.9 A Stevenson screen, containing meteorological instruments for the measurement of air temperature.

You will meet the IPCC soon, but first an easy question. If you wanted to test claims about global warming, how would you go about taking the temperature of the planet? Actually, this is not an easy question at all. Climate varies both spatially (from region to region) and temporally (most obviously by time of day and season), so there is no single or simple way to measure global temperature. It is necessary to compile many measurements of air temperature (Figure 1.9) made over time and in different places and derive an 'average'.

A regional example of this process of compilation was the Asia–Pacific Network for Global Change Research Workshop held in New Zealand in 2001. Meteorologists from around the Pacific brought their national measurements together to produce a composite picture of Pacific climate from 1950 to 2000. According to the convenor, climate scientist Jim Salinger, the results show a higher-than-expected warming in the South Pacific. 'For the whole of the last century, the global average temperature rise was 0.6 °C,' he announced, 'but in the Pacific, temperatures rose higher than that in the second half of the century alone'. The daily temperature records of Australia, the Cook Islands, Fiji, French Polynesia, New Caledonia, the Solomon Islands and Vanuatu show a rise of 0.5–1.0 °C in the second half of the 20th century; elsewhere in the Pacific, the warming was closer to that of the global average. As Salinger, rather sardonically, concluded on behalf of his fellow workshop participants, 'global warming is alive and well' (Musumba, 2001).

But is it? The Pacific covers a vast area, but how can we tell if warming in this region is typical of the whole planet? This brings us to the role of the Intergovernmental Panel on Climate Change (IPCC). The IPCC is a group of scientists assembled under the auspices of the United Nations with a remit to coordinate and collate climate-change evidence from around the world. When its report was released in 2001, it was the most extensive and detailed climate modelling exercise ever achieved.

What was the IPCC's conclusion? Basically, it was the same as that of the Asia–Pacific Network for Global Change Research Workshop. The IPCC argued not only that global climate change is occurring, but also that the Earth is warming at a faster rate than was previously expected. It predicted that temperatures could rise by as much as 5.8 °C by the end of the 21st century (IPCC, 2001a, p. 575). But identifying the warming trend was not enough. To substantiate the claim that climate change is a legitimate environmental problem, the IPCC had to agree on the main cause. Its verdict? Human activity is responsible for most of the problem, with industrial pollution, and in particular gas emissions, as the worst offender.

1.4.1 Contesting the claims

While climate change looks like very bad news for people on low-lying islands, at least having a large international panel of scientists to substantiate the claim of global warming would seem to ensure world opinion is on the side of the Maldivians and other islanders. Unfortunately, finding supporting scientific evidence is rarely this simple. There are many people and groups around the world who remain sceptical about the link between climate change and human activities. And they too have scientists to back their claims.

Earlier doubters tended to discount climate change altogether, and there were scientists prepared to argue that climate had not changed significantly over recent centuries. More recent sceptics are willing to admit that climate change is occurring, but are not satisfied that human activity is the main cause. Statistician Bjorn Lomborg, writing in 2001, conceded that 'the temperature of the late twentieth century is greater than in many previous centuries'. But he went on to state, 'this cannot be taken as a simple indication of overwhelming global warming as we are also coming out of a Little Ice Age' (Lomborg, 2001, p. 263).

Lomborg was suggesting that the observed patterns of warming had more to do with naturally occurring long-term fluctuations than they did with human activity. Other scientists have argued that changes in energy output from the sun are the most likely culprits for global warming. Whatever we wish to make of such claims, these sceptics raise an important point: there is no simple baseline against which we can measure 'deviation' of global temperature from 'normal'. The Earth's temperature fluctuates according to rhythms with different time-scales, including daily temperature cycles and the annual rhythm of the seasons. Other rhythms are less regular and occur at longer time-scales, from decades up to the millennia over which glacial and interglacial cycles occur.

Trying to ascertain whether the planet's climate is showing an increase in extreme weather events is another question that comes up against the 'background noise' of the Earth's natural variability. It has been argued that parts of the world are becoming prone to more intense storms, and that the frequency and intensity of floods, droughts and fires caused by dryness is rising. Once again, the question arises of just what exactly constitutes a 'normal' storm, or an 'ordinary' rainy season. In this case, the IPCC concedes that current observations are not complete or reliable enough to show *any* global trends over the past 50 years. The best it can say is that its models suggest that increases in high wind speeds and extremes of rainfall are 'likely over some areas' (IPCC, 2001a, Section 9.3.6, Table 9.6, p. 575).

So how do we know that the documented trends have more to do with the contributions of human beings than with the normal variation of global temperature? At this stage in the course, we have not examined the evidence with enough depth to take sides. What we can point out is that the scientists involved in the Asia–Pacific workshop and the IPCC were fully aware of this background of naturally occurring fluctuations and took these into account in their calculations of the human contribution to climate change. With regard to some, but not all, observations of climatic variation they felt confident about distinguishing human impacts from 'naturally' occurring fluctuations.

1.4.2 Hard evidence, shaky ground

If determining climate change is complicated, then surely measuring sea-level is simpler? There might be high tides and low tides, but shouldn't we be able to tell if the highest tides are getting higher? The raising of sea-level is one of the most feared aspects of global warming for inhabitants of the low-lying parts of the planet. Heating expands the volume of water, and global warming would be expected to result in a rise in the level of the planet's seas and oceans. At the same time the melting of glaciers is also adding water to overall sea-level (Figure 1.10).

Figure 1.10 An Antarctic glacier calving icebergs into the sea.

Environmental activists argue that climate-induced sea-level change is already underway. Greenpeace claims that two islets from the Kiribati archipelago in the west Pacific have already disappeared. As you probably guessed from the discussion above, sceptics can attribute these observed changes to the natural fluctuations in the Earth's climate — attributing them to the warming occurring independently of human influence.

The IPCC has taken account of this 'background rate' in its modelling of sea-level change. It estimates a sea-level rise of about 5 mm per year — between two and four times higher than the rate in the past 100 years (estimated at 1.0–2.5 mm per year). However, the complexity of its models means that predictions for the future cover a large range of possibilities. At the high end is an increase of 88 cm by the year 2100, while the minimum estimate is 9 cm (IPCC, 2001a, p. 16). These values gives a middle range around 50 cm. The IPCC spells out what this means for low-lying islands:

> Many small island nations are only a few meters above present sea-level. These states may face serious threat of permanent inundation from sea-level rise. Among the most vulnerable of these island states are the Marshall Islands, Kiribati, Tuvalu, Tonga, the Federated States of Micronesia, and the Cook Islands (in the Pacific Ocean); Antigua and Nevis (in the Caribbean Sea); and the Maldives (in the Indian Ocean).
>
> (IPCC, 2001c)

Or, to be more specific:

> An 80-cm sea-level rise could inundate two-thirds of the Marshall Islands and Kiribati.
>
> A 90-cm sea-level rise could cause 85% of Male, the capital of the Maldives, to be inundated.
>
> (IPPC, 2001c)

Does the evidence support the predictions of the model, so far? Even given the range covered by the IPCC, there are scientists who believe there is no evidence of observable acceleration of sea-level rise. That is, none beyond that which could be expected to result from natural climatic variability. Scientists from the National Tidal Facility (NTF) of Flinders University, South Australia have shown that over the last 25 years there has been no change in average sea-level. As the NTF Director Dr Wolfgang Scherer put it: 'There is no acceleration in sea-level rise — none that we can discern, at all' (Amos, 2000).

At the moment, we are neither trying to prove nor disprove claims about global climate change. Our intention is to demonstrate that 'proof' of the existence of environmental change using seemingly straightforward measurements can be very contentious. For complex issues such as global climate change, where numerous variables are involved, there are many opportunities for scientists to take issue with the findings of their colleagues. They can disagree about the procedures for gathering data, the completeness or coverage of data, the ways in which the data are analysed, and then finally the conclusions. Perhaps most importantly, they can take issue with the assumptions upon which entire research programs are based. The theoretical framework that shapes a particular program of research and decides the kind of questions that will be asked can be no less contentious than the quality of data gathered.

Such contention does not make science any less important to the understanding of the environmental issues. In a way, it is the very fact that different researchers are constantly taking each other to task that gives us confidence when the majority of the scientific community finally agrees on something. Consensus doesn't mean that the conclusions are final and will be accepted for all time. But at least we know that if an idea or a theory has had a rocky road on the way to being accepted, then it has had a thorough critical appraisal.

But we are not yet through with potential sources of variation. We have seen that some scientists argue that observable changes in sea-level can be put down to the varying temperatures that are part of the normal variance of our planet's climate. As if this is not complicated enough already, there is another potential source of disagreement amongst scientists who are trying to keep tabs on sea-level.

You may have seen this coming. Not only do the oceans have their own natural fluctuations, the land itself does not stay still. In the late 1960s, scientists proved that the continents float on molten rock (mantle) and drift over the Earth. This finding gives rise to another source of long-term variability. If you think of stepping onto a raft floating on water, it will sit lower. If you step off it will quickly rise back to its previous level. But, if you could look really carefully at what the raft did as you stepped off, you would see it 'bounce' to a level above the previous equilibrium point and then descend to below that level, before bouncing back up again. Successive oscillations are damped and quickly the raft reaches the level it floated at before you stepped on it. During the last ice age large areas of the continents were covered in heavy ice — this made them sit lower in the mantle. At the end of the ice ages when the ice melted, the continent would bounce up in the same way that the raft did in our example above. The difficulty is that the oscillations of the land back to its previous level are very slow. In the United Kingdom, Scotland is still rising a few mm a year following the melting of the ice at the end of the last ice age. At the same time, the south of England is sinking by the same amount as the UK returns to equilibrium.

With this in mind, you can see why it may be difficult to distinguish rising seas from sinking lands. As Wolfgang Scherer put it:

> ...for us, the major uncertainty is land movement. All the historical records of sea-level measure only relative sea-level. If you have a land-mass that is rising, it will look like a lowering of sea-level. Inversely, if the land is sinking, it looks like the sea is rising.
>
> (Amos, 2000)

If continents move, then what about small islands? Aside from coral atolls — which are built up from the once-living bodies of small marine organisms — all other oceanic islands have been formed as a result of the instability of the Earth's crust, either by volcanic activity or upheavals as continental plates bump into each other. What is more, it may be changes in sea-level that actually bring an island above the surface of the sea in the first place!

Small islands are more turbulent and unstable than continents. Whether we are talking about biological processes that build coral islands, or the geological processes that forge 'rocky' islands, these processes carry on and continue long after human beings and other land-based species have made the island their home. As a final blow, it is the fate of all islands, in the very long term, to be worn down by the forces of wave and wind — to be gradually washed and ground, over the millennia back down to the ocean floor from which they arose.

You should now complete the activity associated with this chapter, if not completed earlier.

1.4.3 The challenge of uncertainty

Throughout the previous sections we have been looking at the way that bold statements about the current and future state of the planet usually turn out to be not quite so clear and certain when we look more closely at all the factors involved. This brings us to **uncertainty**: the third of our 'course themes'. It is now widely recognized that uncertainty constantly intrudes into the understanding of environmental problems and the search for solutions. Some of this uncertainty is due to the incompleteness of our knowledge at the moment, and it is to be expected that this sort of uncertainty might well give way to greater confidence at some time in the future, when more data are available. As we have seen, enormous effort is now going into the gathering, processing and analysing of information about the state of the planet's climatic systems, all with the aim of reducing uncertainty.

But not all uncertainty can be overcome by better data or by debates over the best way to interpret this data. Some forms of uncertainty are due to the fact that the many events or processes simply do not unfold in a predictable way. This is the case where many different factors are involved, each influencing the others — in such a way that the outcome is something genuinely novel: an outcome that cannot be predicted on account of what has been observed in the past. This sort of uncertainty occurs at the small everyday level — think, for example, of the difficulty of predicting the exact outcome of any sports match — or any casual conversation. But it is also the case, on a much larger scale, with most major environmental problems, which involve a unique coming together of a range of factors and circumstances.

What this means is that uncertainty is unavoidable: it is both part of the world and part of our understanding of the world. And in this sense, uncertainty should not prevent us from making decisions about environmental problems. What is vital is to be clear and up-front about both the strengths and the limitations of our knowledge claims. Box 1.1, which you should read now, looks at how the IPCC deals with uncertainty.

Box 1.1 How the IPCC addresses uncertainty

The IPCC indicates the degree of confidence or uncertainty it has in its conclusions by dividing its findings into four main categories (IPCC, 2001b, p. 24):

Well-established: models incorporate known processes; observations are consistent with models; or multiple lines of evidence support the finding.

Established but incomplete: models incorporate most known processes, although some parameterizations may not be well tested; observations are somewhat consistent but incomplete; current empirical estimates are well founded, but the possibility of changes in governing processes over time is considerable; or only one or a few lines of evidence support the finding.

Competing explanations: different model representations account for different aspects of observations or evidence or incorporate different aspects of key processes, leading to competing explanations.

Speculative: conceptually plausible ideas that haven't received much attention in the literature or that are laced with difficult-to-reduce uncertainty.

You will hear more about the different types and degrees of uncertainty as the course proceeds. And you will find out more about the implications of uncertainty for different areas of environmental decision-making. For now, let's turn to one of the major uncertainties that haunt the issue of global climate change.

You might recall that both newspaper articles on the Maldives made reference to the melting of the ice of Antarctica. For climate-change scientists, what is at issue here is the possible collapse of the part of the ice cap called the West Antarctic Ice-Sheet (WAIS) (Figure 1.11). If the WAIS collapsed it would result in a rise in global sea-level of some 5 m over a short time-span. There is evidence to suggest that it has broken up previously, long before human impact could have played a part. It is not yet fully understood why this happened, though researchers recognize that it was triggered by a complex interaction between the various components of the climate system. Even if a previous collapse of the WAIS could be explained, this would not necessarily provide us with a clear understanding of the present predicament. This is because we are dealing with a hugely complex system, in which it is very difficult to isolate the effects of different factors. The fact that human-induced impacts comprise a whole new variable only makes prediction based on past experience even more difficult. Box 1.2, which you should read now, introduces the concept of catastrophic change.

Figure 1.11 The West Antarctic Ice-Sheet.

Box 1.2 Understanding a collapse or 'catastrophic' change

When climate change scientists talk about a 'collapse' in the WAIS, what they mean is a rapid change from one state to another. Such changes occur in many systems, of various kinds. These are sometimes called **'catastrophic' changes**, as it is very difficult, or impossible, for the system to return to the original state.

Sometimes a system responds gradually to changes, little by little and step by step, as shown by the ball bearing on a table in Figure 1.12. If you were to give the ball bearing a small push, it would roll a short way and then stop. This is our gradual change in the ball bearing 'system'.

Figure 1.12 A ball bearing on a flat table.

However, sometimes you can keep giving the ball bearing small pushes and it comes to a steep drop (Figure 1.13). If you nudge the ball bearing 'over the edge', it gathers momentum until it hits the floor. The drop is rapid and very hard to reverse.

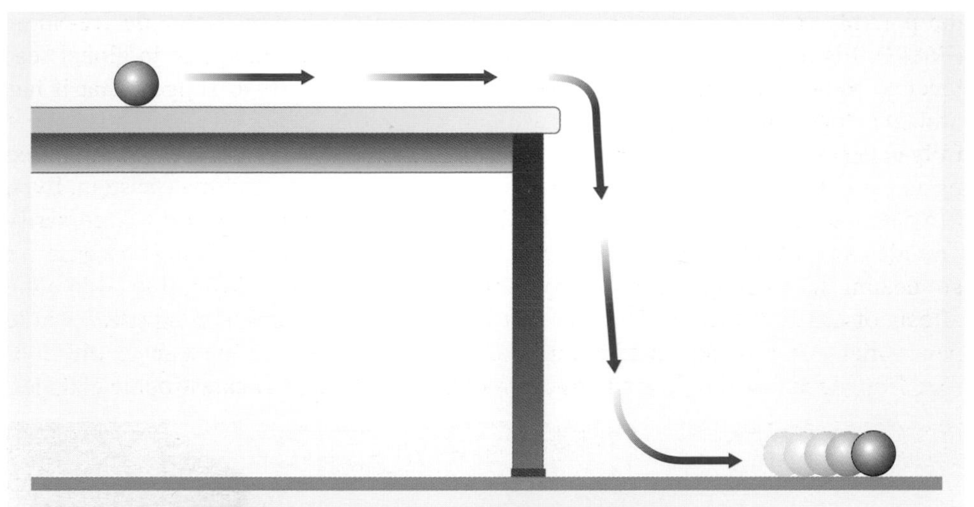

Figure 1.13 A ball bearing dropping over a steep drop on a table.
In this scenario, the ball bearing system has two 'stable' states. One stable state is composed of the range of movements on the table top. This state is lost once the ball bearing goes over the edge. When it reaches the floor, the system enters an alternative 'stable state', which is composed of the range of movements at this lower level. We say the system has 'collapsed', or undergone a 'catastrophic' change. By catastrophic we don't necessarily mean bad for humans. Such shifts happen at various scales all around us and all the time.

Although the ball bearing is a very simple example, it is now known that many systems in the natural and social world change in this way. For example, the WAIS appears to be part of system that has two stable states — the ice-sheet there, and the ice-sheet gone. The question is when, and what is the likelihood of the 'drop'? Pressures leading to a transformation might be building up, but there are often no visible signs that a shift is coming (the drop in Figure 1.13).

So what are the chances that human-induced climate change might be pushing the WAIS towards collapse? The best the IPCC can suggest is a 'low-to-medium confidence' prediction that rapid and large temperature increases will result in a large-scale collapse, though it has concluded that this collapse is very unlikely to happen over the next century. This finding comes under the 'Established but incomplete' category in Box 1.1. Such a respite does not clear today's heavy energy users of responsibility, however. In the case of the WAIS, as with many systems prone to catastrophic changes, there may be a considerable time-lag between the pressures building up to a change, and the change actually occurring. Current human contributions to climate change, the IPCC points out, might not make themselves fully felt in Antarctica for centuries or even millennia.

1.5 Sustainability in a dynamic world

As we saw earlier in the chapter, there is a tendency to think about islands as 'Edens', or pristine, undisturbed places. To think about islands, or any other sort of landscape in this way, is to imply that everything was perfect in the beginning. But islands usually have turbulent beginnings, and continue to be shaped and changed by dynamic processes throughout their existence (Figure 1.14, overleaf). And this is the case, to varying degrees, for all land-forms, insular and continental.

Figure 1.14 White Island, New Zealand, an island formed by volcanic activity.

The dynamism of the natural world means that there is no state of perfection — no stable baseline against which to measure human-induced changes. It also means that it is often extremely difficult to distinguish human-induced or '**anthropogenic**' changes from the background of ongoing variation and change. Even on a relatively brief time-scale, taking in a normal day and night — there are changes in temperature and light, and in the activity of living things. On a much longer time-scale, landmasses buckle and shift, great plates of ice advance and retreat, and the oceans rise and fall. In the very, very long term, stars eventually burn out and die.

But what does this mean for the ideal of sustainability. Sustainability, as we saw in Section 1.2, is about living without undermining the conditions, processes and resources that support life. So how can we tell if our demands on the physical and living systems we rely on are too great? In the short term, we often seem to get away with quite extravagant demands on natural systems. But because of the way that changes of state occur in systems, this may simply mean that the eventual effects are not yet visible. In the long term, as the saying goes, we are all dead. Even without human impacts, changes in the physical systems that all life relies on will eventually render life, as we know it, unsustainable.

What this means is that time-scales are crucial when we are thinking about sustainability. The implication of inhabiting a world with many different rhythms of change and variance is that human impacts must always be addressed in a context of other forces and processes, many of which operate at scales that greatly exceed our every day 'common sense' perceptions.

One of the great challenges that environmentalists face is to disentangle human-induced change from natural processes, and to identify the sources of these anthropogenic transformations. In this regard, as we have seen, scientific evidence plays a vital role.

But at the same time, the complex interplay of many dynamic processes means that, even with massive investments in research, there will always be uncertainties. It is one thing to acknowledge uncertainty, however, and quite another to actually live in the light of this knowledge. Taking uncertainty into consideration — working with it, through it and around it — is a central part of the environmental challenge.

This uncertainty raises important questions for the concept of sustainability. What exactly are we trying to 'sustain' in a world that both gives and takes away resources for living in great sweeping motions of its own? What sort of goals should we choose to develop or progress towards, once we have become aware that the goalposts are bound to shift, or that the whole playing field might tilt or crumple? Whatever course of action is chosen, we can be assured that new challenges will always arise. This is one reason why you should be deeply suspicious of any 'final solutions' to long-term environmental issues or to the broader question of how human beings should best interact with the rest of the natural world.

The variability of the planet, and the uncertainty that goes with it, means that all people wherever they live are to some degree vulnerable to changes in their environment. Human disturbance tends to add to this vulnerability — often making the already vulnerable much more so. As the precarious situation of the Maldivians and others living on low-lying areas makes clear, vulnerability is not evenly shared.

While the risk of inundation may be an extreme case, it highlights two crucial issues. One is the need for those who are most vulnerable to have a strong say in world affairs. So far, we have emphasized the importance of 'expert knowledge' to inform the environmental decision-making process — especially where knowledge is needed that exceeds our 'common senses'. However, science can only help us with certain aspects of environmental problems. There are other forms of experience and ways of knowing that are also are also vital. One of the reasons for trying to think about global environmental changes from the point of view of island people was to make it clear that there are different perspectives on environmental problems, and that different groups of people bring differing interests, values and experiences to the debating table.

The second issue, which is related to the first, is the question of responsibility. As the concept of globalization suggests, the things we do in our own, local part of the world can impact on the far side of the globe, and vice versa. In the case of global climate changes, we have seen that many of those who are most vulnerable are paying the price for changes that are not of their own making — while others reap the benefits. This inequity raises the issue of how those who have triggered environmental changes should face the question of their responsibility for the lives of other people — others who may be distant in space, or who may belong to generations still to come.

These are issues that we will be engaging with throughout the course. Before we can face them head on, however, there is more we need to know about the dynamics of our planet, and what they mean for human beings — for the social and cultural life of our species. In the following two chapters, you will be looking more closely at the interface between the living planet and the social world; starting from small scale, localized cases and building up towards the global scale.

1.6 Summary of Chapter 1

1.1 Environmental problems are an important aspect of globalization — a concept that refers to the process and the experience of the increasing interconnectedness of the world.

1.2 Sustainability has emerged as a central issue of contemporary environmentalism in response to the charge that continued economic growth is undermining the long-term life-support systems of the planet.

1.3 The claim that less-developed nations have a right to benefit from economic growth in the same way that developed nations have in the past presents a serious challenge for advocates of sustainability.

1.4 'Sustainable development' makes an explicit connection between environmental issues and issues of global economic inequality. The concept suggests that it is possible to reconcile further social and economic development with environmental protection.

1.5 Mounting evidence about human-induced environmental change at a global scale is a cogent reminder that there is a continuing tension between calls for continued economic growth and environmental sustainability.

1.6 The predicament of people on small islands and other low-lying areas demonstrates that vulnerability to global environmental changes is not evenly distributed. This inequity raises important ethical and political issues about the responsibility of people elsewhere in the world for these threats.

1.7 In the modern world claims about environmental risk and degradation must be backed up by scientific evidence.

1.8 Most of the major claims about human-induced global environmental change are contested to some degree, although there is an emerging consensus over some of the major points.

1.9 One of the main sources of contention is how the distinction should be made between human-induced changes and changes caused by natural variation — such as fluctuations of climate or sea-level and geological instability.

1.10 An added difficulty with tracking the impact of human activities arises because of the patterns of stability of many of the physical and biological systems in question. Because systems may reach a threshold and change their state quite suddenly, it can be difficult to gauge the human contribution to change or to predict when a change of state might occur.

1.11 There are many uncertainties in the state of knowledge about environmental change, both because of inadequacies of the available data and analysis, and because of the inherent unpredictability of some of the systems that are being studied. This means that there will always be a play-off between confidence and uncertainty.

1.12 A sense of the dynamism and turbulence that is part of the natural world itself increasingly forms the backdrop to the sustainability issue — raising questions about what it is we are trying to sustain and how the goals of development should be set.

Learning Outcomes for Chapter 1

When you have completed this chapter, you should be able to:

1.1 Define and use, or recognize definitions and applications of, each of the terms given in **bold** in the text. (Questions 1.1 and 1.9)

1.2 Describe the tensions between development and environmental protection that gave rise to the concept of sustainable development. (Questions 1.2 and 1.3)

1.3 Explain why people living on islands and other low-lying areas are particularly concerned about global climate change. (Questions 1.4 and 1.5)

1.4 Explain why natural variance and instability make it difficult to determine the human contribution to global climate change. (Questions 1.6–1.8)

1.5 Explain why uncertainty about large-scale environmental change might be reduced but not entirely eliminated by the availability of more complete data. (Questions 1.9 and 1.10)

Questions for Chapter 1

Question 1.1

From what you have read in this chapter, which of the following, if any, are useful lessons we should take from the concept of globalization?

(a) Increasing global interconnectivity entails risks as well as opportunities.

(b) Increasing global interconnectivity will make the world a better place.

(c) Today, we are all in the same boat.

(d) The benefits and costs of most forms of global interconnectivity are not evenly shared.

(e) The Internet renders all other media obsolete.

Question 1.2

Explain, in a couple of sentences, why it might be a good idea to place limits on the number of tourists that visit a small island each year.

Question 1.3

Which of the following demands, if any, is the concept of sustainable development intended to satisfy.

(a) That the less-developed world should be able to share the standard of living of the wealthiest countries.

(b) That the developed world should abandon all further economic growth.

(c) That the developed world should lower its standard of living until the less-developed world catches up.

(d) That future generations should have access to the same environmental resources and opportunities as present generations.

Question 1.4

In a maximum of 100 words, compare and contrast the way in which someone living in the British Isles and a Maldivian might view the prospect of a slight global warming.

Question 1.5

Give two examples of the negative effects of rising sea-level on low-lying islands such as the Maldives.

Question 1.6

In a maximum of 100 words, explain why measurements showing steady increases in temperature taken over ten years on a small island would be insufficient proof of human-induced global warming.

Question 1.7

Which of the following statements, if any, could conceivably explain an observed increase in sea-level?

(a) The sea has increased in volume due to human-induced global warming.

(b) The sea has increased in volume due to warming caused by natural fluctuations.

(c) The sea-level has risen because human-induced warming has caused glaciers to melt.

(d) The sea-level has risen because natural warming has caused glaciers to melt.

(e) The land is tilting downwards due to the after-effects of glaciation.

(f) The land is tilting upwards due to the after-effects of glaciation.

(g) The land has subsided due to seismic activity.

Question 1.8

List three factors that could explain how a new tropical oceanic island has come into being.

Question 1.9

Which of the following statements, if any, suggest a *mis*understanding of the implications of uncertainty in the field of environmental change.

(a) Improved data will generally reduce uncertainty.

(b) Much-improved data will eliminate uncertainty.

(c) We can avoid the drawbacks of uncertainty if we remember that there is nothing new under the sun.

(d) A high degree of uncertainty is associated with genuinely novel events.

(e) The presence of uncertainty prevents effective environmental decision-making.

(f) The presence of uncertainty should make us suspicious of 'final' and absolute solutions to environmental problems.

Question 1.10

Which of the following statements, if any, are true about 'catastrophic' changes in the state of a system?

(a) They are difficult to reverse or undo.

(b) They always have disastrous effects on human beings.

(c) There are many warning signs that a change is on the way.

(d) Under normal circumstances, systems with two alternative states are finely balanced between these states.

(e) They are a major source of uncertainty.

References

Amos, J. (2000) *'No Acceleration' in Pacific Sea Rise* [online], BBC News Online. Available from: http://news6.thdo.bbc.co.uk/hi/english/sci/tech/newsid_1035000/1035489.stm [Accessed 17 September 2002].

French, H. (2000) *Vanishing Borders: Protecting the Planet in the Age of Globalization*. New York: Norton.

Giles, B. and Mortimer, H. (1998) *BBC Weather Activity Set*. London: HarperCollins.

Independent Commission on International Development Issues (1980) *North, South, A Programme for Survival*. London: Pan. [Also known as the Brandt Report.]

IPCC (2001a) *Climate Change 2001: The Scientific Basis. Contribution of Working Group I to the Third Assessment Report of the Intergovernmental Panel on Climate Change*. Cambridge: Cambridge University Press.

IPCC (2001b) *Climate Change 2001: Impacts, Adaptation and Vulnerability. Contribution of Working Group II to the Third Assessment Report of the Intergovernmental Panel on Climate Change*. Cambridge: Cambridge University Press.

IPCC (2001c) Threatened small island states. In *Climate Change 2001: Impacts, Adaptation and Vulnerability* [online]. Available from: http://www.unep.no/climate/ipcc_tar/wg2/671.htm [Accessed 2 October 2002].

Lomborg, B. (2001) *The Skeptical Environmentalist: Measuring the Real State of the World*. Cambridge: Cambridge University Press.

Palm Beach, Maldives (1997) [online]. Available from: http://palmbeach-maldives.com/island.htm [Accessed 27 August 2002].

World Commission on Environment and Development (1987) *Our Common Future*. Oxford: Oxford University Press. [Also known as the Brundtland Report.]

Musumba, J. (2001) *Pacific: Pacific Warming Surprises Scientists* [online], Small Island Developing States Network. Available from: http://www.sidsnet.org/archives/climate-newswire/2001/0197.html [Accessed 22 January 2002].

2 Island life: adventures in isolation and openness

Prepared for the course team by Nigel Clark

2

2.1 Introduction

So far we have looked at the geological and climatic transformations that make and remake islands. In focusing on these powerful physical forces we have not yet had much to say about another force that shapes the planet — life itself. While life on Earth may seem dwarfed by the vastness of rock, water and air, it has been calculated that the total mass of all the organisms that have ever lived is somewhere between 1000 and 10 000 times the mass of the Earth itself (Rampino and Caldeira, 1994, p. 103).

For all that living creatures themselves are diverse and fascinating, if our concern is environmental issues, it is ecosystems that are going to be of most interest to us. 'An **ecosystem** is a community of interacting organisms and the physical environment they live in', as the World Resources Institute puts it (2000, p. 10). Ecosystems can be any size: they can be as small as a pond in your garden, or as large as an ocean. Each ecosystem tends to blend into its neighbours and form part of larger ecosystems, expanding to the level of the entire planet.

What makes an ecosystem distinct is a certain integrity that comes from the degree of interconnectivity between its parts. At the same time, every ecosystem is reliant on energy from the outside and on exchanges of organic and inorganic matter with surrounding ecosystems. Human beings have a somewhat ambivalent place with regard to ecosystems. We are part of the ecosystems we dwell in, but we also have our own systems. Our 'social systems' have their own integrity and dynamics, and of course, their own exchanges with other social systems.

In this chapter, we look at the interplay between life and land-form, and between human beings and other forms of life. Islands are a good model because they have distinct boundaries: it is easier to see the exchanges than in ecosystems on larger landmasses. In many cases we also have a fairly clear idea of when human beings first arrived on previously uninhabited islands. In this way, we can get a picture of what happens when groups of people encounter ecosystems when neither is accustomed to the other.

The journeys and migrations that first brought human beings to oceanic islands are the predecessors of today's globalization. In this chapter, we track some cases of human mobility that take us around the planet and back in history, starting with the early European exploration of the world's oceans, then heading back still further in time.

The evidence about human arrival on islands tells a story of the extreme vulnerability of island ecosystems. But the study of island life also demonstrates that islands are sites where life's creativity can be observed with particular clarity (Figure 2.1). 'Island life', in this sense, shows us how vulnerability and change are two sides of the same coin. However, it is not only biological life that adapts and evolves. You will also see that human settlers on islands must adapt their social lives if they too are to survive in the long term. In this chapter we encounter the challenges that a new environment places on human social life, and we start to look at the ways that societies steer or 'govern' their way through these challenges.

Figure 2.1 Island ecosystems: water plants and lowland forest at Waimea Falls, Oahu, Hawaii.

2.2 Tropical island Edens

From around the 14th century onwards, Europeans set out on a great wave of maritime exploration. They were not, however, the first people to make long voyages. With one notable exception (of which you will hear more in the second half of this book), all the world's large landmasses had been settled, and a great many small islands had been visited or colonized. But there were still 'unknown' islands, and these came to play an important strategic role in European expansion.

When European mariners first came across fertile and uninhabited islands in the midst of the oceans, such as St Helena, Cape Verde, the Azores and the Madeiras in the Atlantic, and Mauritius in the Indian Ocean (Figure 2.2), it must have seemed to them like divine providence. As a Dutch voyager described St Helena in 1589:

> The water is excellently good and falleth down from the mountains and so runneth in great abundance by small channels to the sea...that it seemed a wonder wrought by God...it is an earthly paradise for the Portuguese ships and seemeth to have been miraculously discovered for the refreshing and servicing of the same, considering the smallness and highness of the land, lying in the middle of the Ocean seas...
>
> (cited in Grove, 1995, p. 98)

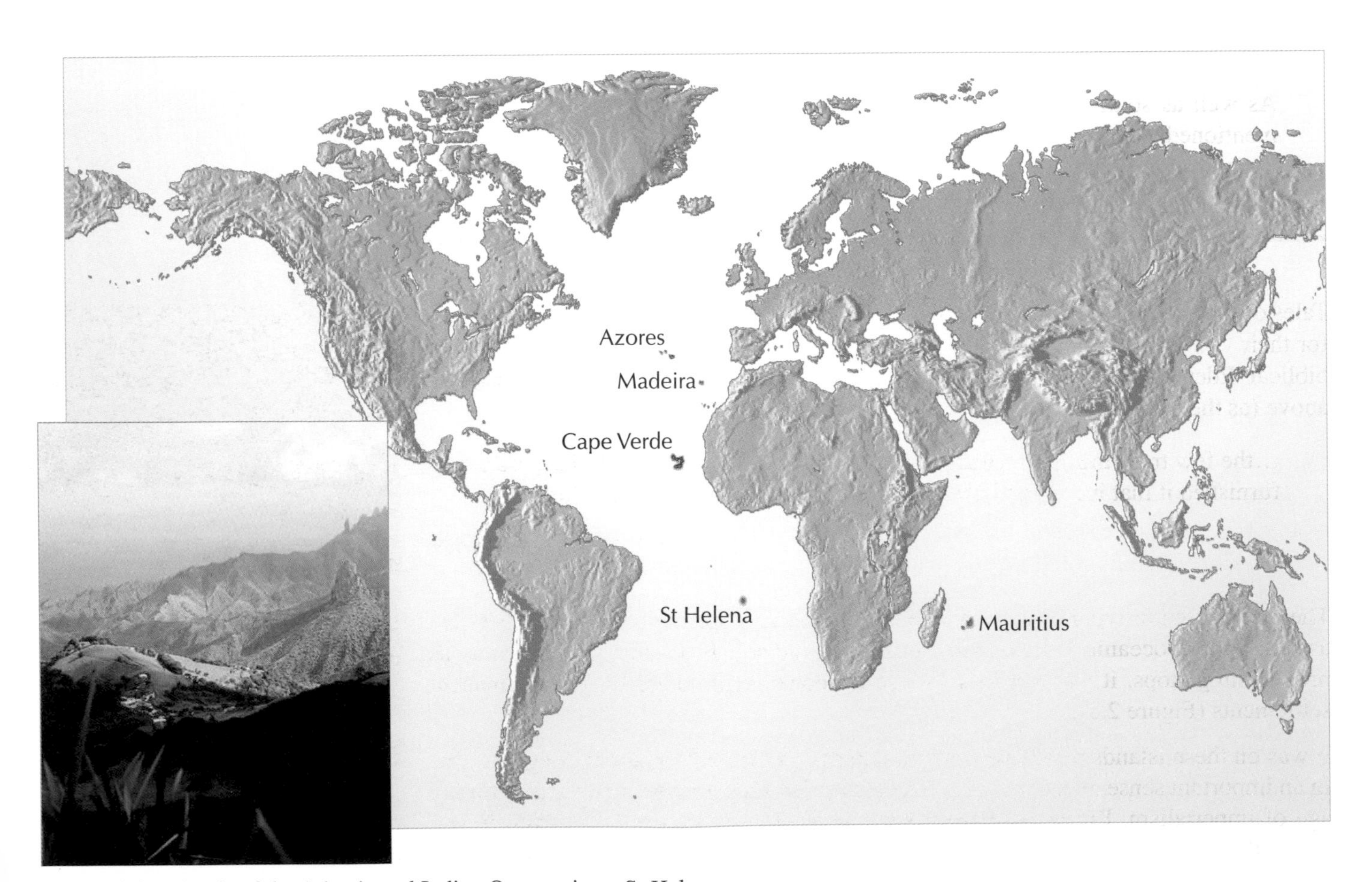

Figure 2.2 Islands of the Atlantic and Indian Oceans; inset St Helena.

Activity 2.1 Island stopovers

Put yourself in the role of a ship's crew member in the 17th century, coming across an island in the middle of an arduous voyage. Remember seafarers went for months without fresh food, and diseases such as scurvy (caused by vitamin C deficiency) were the bane of long voyages. In the best of all possible worlds, what would you hope to gain from an island stopover? Jot down a few ideas.

Comment

Now compare your notes with the account of St Helena provided by J. A. von Mandelslo, a 17th-century traveller from Holstein (now in Germany) on his way to India:

> At this place a man may at any time of the year [find] figs and pomegranates; citrus and oranges are there, also goats...barbary hens, pheasants, partridges, quails, peacocks, pigeons; and great stocks of all sorts of birds, as also salt for the keeping of them, so that ships may be sufficiently provided with all things if they would stay there any time. The sea supplies with more fish than can be consumed, and the earth brings forth so many excellent herbs, that the Portuguez, unwilling to retard their voyage, leave at this place their sick men, who recover their health within a few days and having only a little Oyl, rice byskets and spice, make a shift to live there till the ships come hither next year.
>
> (cited in Grove, spelling as in original, 1995, p. 43)

As well as some of the points our 17th-century voyager noted, you may have mentioned others. Like sex, for example. Sexual liaisons were clearly not a feature of uninhabited islands, but they were certainly a major attraction for early European visitors to some Pacific islands.

Tales of lush, verdant islands thrilled sailors and armchair travellers alike — not only for their practical value, but because these 'enchanted isles' reminded people of the biblical 'Eden'. You may have noticed that some of the trees and animals in the account above (as the writer was aware) had been brought in by earlier visitors:

> ...the few trees they planted and the little stock of cattle they left there hath so furnished it that it is...sufficient to refresh all the fleets that come hither.
>
> (cited in Grove, 1995, p. 43)

The unexpected thriving of these unattended introduced species served to bolster the association of oceanic islands with 'earthly paradise'. From using the islands as provisioning stops, it was not long before European visitors established permanent settlements (Figure 2.3).

Figure 2.3 A late 16th-century print of Dutch colonists on Mauritius.

It was on these islands that Europeans first experimented with plantation agriculture. In an important sense, these trial runs in colonization prepared the way for the coming age of imperialism. But as permanent settlement progressed, the idea of fertile and Eden-like islands took a serious blow. In a few decades, or even less, settlers began to notice that their activities were having seriously damaging effects on the environment of the islands that were so crucial to their maritime ventures.

Some of the first problems documented were the effects of deforestation. A visiting French scientist reported of 18th-century Mauritius:

> Reckless and ignorant men, thinking of nothing but themselves, have ravaged the island, destroying the trees by fire to make a fortune for themselves at the expense of the colony, leaving nothing for their successors but arid lands abandoned by rain and exposed without relief to storms and the burning sun.
>
> (cited in Grove, 1995, p. 202)

Island inhabitants observed the effect of clearing forests on soil cover. The official 18th-century records in St Helena noted that 'the weather breaks and washes away the soil till the naked rocks appear' (cited in Grove, 1995, p. 121). This eroding soil then silted up rivers and harbours and contaminated water supplies. Not surprisingly, being surrounded by thousands of miles of salty ocean, any threat to an island's fresh water supply was a vital issue. Very early on, informed observers were giving serious consideration to the idea that deforestation had a deleterious effect on mist and rainfall, and hence on water supplies. By the mid-18th century, theories about human-induced climate change were widespread amongst island administrators, and it was broadly accepted that deforestation posed a serious threat to the whole colonial project.

2.3 Threats to island life

European settlers on oceanic islands, in other words, were learning a hard lesson about unsustainable development. However, it was not only concern with climate change and deforestation that came early to these small islands — the early settlers and visitors began to develop a basic, hands-on understanding of their impact on the biological life of islands. At least half a century before Charles Darwin would glean his valuable insights on the origins of species from the Galapagos Islands, colonial scientists on islands such as Mauritius and St Helena had a clear sense of the peculiar qualities of island biota. And more importantly, a sense of its susceptibility to human-induced changes. Francois Leguat, a member of a French expedition to Mauritius at the end of the 17th century, recounted that 'this island fairly abounded with Wild Geese and Ducks, Moorhens, Quails, Sea and Land Tortoises, but now all these have become scarce' (cited in Grove, 1995, p. 151).

Figure 2.4 An early 17th-century painting of the dodo.

One of the first examples of the vulnerability of island wildlife was the infamous case of the dodo, *Raphus cucullatus* (Figure 2.4). The large, flightless bird was **endemic** to Mauritius — in other words, it was found there and nowhere else. Adapted to life on an island with no human occupants or terrestrial mammals, the dodo had little need for 'fight or flight' and when faced with new threats its behaviour tended to be incautious or naive. It was also a ground-nester, laying a single egg per clutch.

Widespread hunting was not, however, the worst of the dodo's problems. The success of introduced domestic animals may have been a boon to human settlers, but astute observers soon noted a downside to their extraordinary proliferation. Leguat surmised the main agent of destruction on Mauritius. As he wrote of the pigs that had been introduced to the island: 'these beasts do a great deal of damage to the inhabitants, by devouring all the young animals they catch' (cited in Grove, 1995, p. 151). The problem of the destructive spread of introduced species that Leguat identified is now known as **bioinvasion**. Recent research supports his conclusion, but adds a second culprit. A species of monkey from southeast Asia — the crab-eating macaque — was also introduced (perhaps accidentally) to Mauritius, where it reproduced prolifically. Archaeological evidence suggests that both pigs and monkeys preyed on the eggs and the young of *Raphus cucullatus*.

The last eyewitness account of dodos came from Dutch sailors shipwrecked on Mauritius in 1662, only 155 years after the islands were first sighted by Europeans. The dodo had already vanished from the main island, but one was spotted — and subsequently spitted — by the hungry castaways on a small islet off the coast: perhaps just far enough off to hold pigs and monkeys at bay. Presumably, at some moment not long after the sailors were rescued, on a sliver of land probably too small to support a viable population, the last dodo quietly expired (Quammen, 1996).

The dodo found its way into the European bestiary of wondrous exotic creatures, where it has been — rather unfairly — characterized as fat, stupid and sluggardly. Reports of its extinction had considerable impact, as it was the first time that Europeans were aware of an animal disappearing off the face of the planet.

2.4 Lessons from small islands

Aside from the phrase 'dead as a dodo' and the sorry story it commemorates, it is remarkable how little of the environmental history of Europe's oceanic island colonies has made its way into today's environmental consciousness — particularly when we consider the common concerns.

From the account of European impacts on islands above, how many problems can you recognize that are also contemporary issues. See if you can give six examples.

You may have thought of:

- deforestation
- soil erosion
- watershed deterioration and fresh-water pollution
- climate change
- loss of biological diversity, including total extinction
- bioinvasion

Some of these problems are, of course, closely related. The main point is that there are important parallels between the impacts deriving from early European movement around the planet, and the environmental problems associated with the more intensive global movements and exchanges of today's world. What the evidence from the settlement of uninhabited islands points to is the relationship between global movement and the problem of sustainability. Europeans who settled on small tropical islands were entering environments very different from those they were familiar with at home. This transition meant that the knowledge and the skills they brought with them had a high chance of being unsuited to the places they colonized — thus greatly increasing the risk that the activities they engaged in would be unsustainable in the long term.

Another way of putting this would be to say that at the point of their arrival, European knowledge of tropical islands and their ecosystems was extremely incomplete.

We would now recognize this as a case of high uncertainty. But at the time, Europeans tended to be quite confident that their way of doing things was the best of all possible ways, and hence appropriate all over the world. The implication of this was that their levels of confidence often far exceeded the data they had available — resulting in a succession of risky and unsustainable practices. What greatly exacerbated this situation is the fact that many of the vital decisions about island 'improvement' were made back in the centres of European power — at the head offices of merchant companies or at seats of government.

Over time, however, some European colonists on small islands became very aware of their mistakes. As we have seen, they observed the changes they were bringing about, and in many cases they changed their behaviour quite markedly. Indeed, environmental historian Richard Grove has argued that an early form of 'environmental' awareness arose out of the experience of the degradation of small island colonies. This resulted in some pioneering legislation in an attempt to mitigate the damage that was being done (Grove, 1995). Just as groups of environmentally conscious people are today attempting to steer their societies away from destructive practices, so too did alliances of island administrators, settlers and visiting scientists attempt to reset the course of the small tropical islands, several centuries ago.

The question of 'steering' societies brings us to the notion of **governance** — the fourth and final of our course themes. Governance is a term that refers to all the means by which various people or groups attempt to control, manage or set the course of their societies. The term comes from *kubernetes*, the ancient Greek word for helmsman, a reference to the fact that running a society is a bit like keeping a ship on course through shifting winds and swells. 'Government' has the same root, but has the connotation of elites or experts managing from above — and sending their directives from 'the top down'. The concept of governance, by contrast, is much more encompassing — taking in all the different 'actors' who can make a difference to the way a society or state is run, all the way from the 'bottom' to the top.

With regard to the 'steering' of small island colonies, we can describe the role of state bodies and boards of company directors far away in the capitals of Europe as a form of govern*ment* — enacted through local representatives on the islands. However, in cases when these local representatives took note of what was happening locally and attempted to set a different course for the island colonies, we might better speak of govern*ance* than govern*ment*. In some cases, local attempts to make island agriculture more sustainable led to disagreement and conflict with directors back at head office. What is important to note is that those with experience of events 'on the ground' were often able to make a difference — helped by the fact that the people 'at the top' were usually a considerable sea voyage away.

It is also worth noting that voyaging scientists also played an important part in the emergence of early environmental sensibilities. Travelling by sea, they were able to 'network' between one island and another, and in this way provided an alternative flow of information to the top-down flow from European centres to their colonies (Grove, 1995, pp. 74, 137–8). So while the Internet might be very important to environmentalists today, it is not the first 'global network' of environmental data and ideas!

Now would be a good time to begin the Web activities associated with this chapter.

2.5 Environmentalism and the idea of 'Eden'

As Grove points out, the relevance of this early form of 'environmentalism' to the rest of the world was not apparent at the time. He concludes: 'there are very few indications that contemporary observers believed that the kinds of environmental changes observed on oceanic islands could also happen on a continental scale' (1995, p. 365). The intervening history of European expansion is complex and messy, and it is difficult to trace a line of descent from early environmental awareness on small islands to the consciousness and activism of today.

There is, however, one very significant way in which the experience of tropical islands has been passed on, all the way to the present.

- Does the imagery of the early European visitors remind you of anything you have already encountered in this course?
- The portrayal of tropical islands as an 'earthly paradise' anticipates the references to 'Eden' and undisturbed perfection that feature in the Palm Beach Island promotion (Section 1.3).

Activity 2.2

But what are these common features of the earliest and the latest depictions of tropical island paradises? Jot down your ideas. See if you can come up with two or three points.

Comment

The biblical idea of 'Eden' (Figure 2.5), which both past and contemporary island imagery revisits, includes an extraordinary diversity of living creatures, and such an abundance of the resources for good living that labour is scarcely required ('fruit' tends to feature prominently for just this reason). The scenario is relaxing, healthy, even curative, and the climate is always pleasant — a sort of 'perpetual spring'. And of course we want this world pretty much to ourselves: uninhabited islands and the near-deserted beaches of the holiday brochure make a virtue of no competition with others to enjoy paradise.

Figure 2.5 A painting of the Garden of Eden.

All this ruminating over 'enchanted' islands may seem like a digression from the pressing issues of sustainable development and global poverty. But we should not make light of its significance, for the Eden idea is as deeply embedded in contemporary environmentalism as it is in the historic voyaging literature or the modern tourist industry.

Keep in mind that even five or six centuries ago, there were few vestiges of truly wild or uncultivated land in Europe. Previously uninhabited islands were a taste of what the world could have been like without humans, or 'before the fall'. So, islands played a vital role in cementing the view that the ideal landscape was one devoid of human presence. The degradation and even collapse of entire island ecosystems after settlement only served to reinforce the idea of the fall, the notion that human impact entailed a corruption of the purity and perfection of nature.

Uninhabited oceanic islands were, in effect, the first 'new worlds' encountered by Europeans and so had a huge effect on their imagination. Once the precedent was set that the original state of nature was without visible human impact, explorers and colonists from Europe continued to conceive of all newly discovered worlds as 'virgin' lands. Unfortunately this was the case even if these lands already had peoples of their own. As Europeans penetrated the American continent, the idea of the undefiled **wilderness** was still further entrenched. As in the case of early oceanic islands, celebrations of human 'improvement' of the landscape were tempered by feelings of loss, and nostalgia for the once-perfect world that was being effaced. Wherever 'wilderness' was perceived as the ideal state of nature, there was deep discomfort over its defilement. This view was to become a mainstay of modern environmentalism, no less than it was to emerge as a key ingredient of the tourist industry.

This idea of the original perfection of nature and a subsequent fall caused by humankind has a deep emotional appeal, at least in the western world. But is this a useful point of departure for modern environmental issues?

- Based on the discussion of environmental issues in Chapter 1, what do you think the shortcomings of the undefiled wilderness idea might be?
- The natural world is subject to constant change and fluctuation. The perfect wilderness idea suggests a static state where everything is in balance and in its proper, given place.

Taking nature's dynamic qualities seriously challenges this sense of harmony, but it does not imply that 'anything goes'.

Of course, there is nothing new about the idea that the natural world is in constant change. Geological change gained acceptance in the late 18th century. This idea of change was extended to biological life with the rise of evolutionary theory in the mid-19th century. However, geological change and biological evolution were viewed as imperceptibly slow in relation to the dramatic pace at which humans could transform the natural world. In the popular imagination, the contrast between nature's gradualism and humankind's frenetic activity sustained the idea that natural world was perfectly adjusted — until human tampering nudged it out of balance.

As we have seen, this idea of the perfection of islands does not sit well with the knowledge that oceanic islands have, at some stage, been thrust into existence by geological activity. So too does a closer look at the biological life of islands render problematic the idea that islands were perfect to start with.

- What do you think is the main problem with the 'Edenic' view of island life?
- Just as human beings had to cross the sea to colonize oceanic islands, so did all other forms of life.

2.6 Islands and the origin of species

Far from starting off as 'pure' or 'undefiled' Edens, the reality is that encroachment or invasion by species is an essential part of the making and remaking of island ecosystems. This is a chancy business. Relative to the area of oceans, islands are tiny and few, with the challenge of a sea-crossing sorting the occasional winners from the vast multitude of losers. If sex is the preferred means of reproduction, the need for a pair, or at least a pregnant female, means the odds of a successful colonizing skyrocket still further.

Charles Darwin was fascinated by the question of how terrestrial species colonized oceanic islands. Where some scientists postulated lost 'sea bridges' connecting islands to continents, Darwin argued in *The Origin of Species* in 1859 that fluctuations in sea-level could not explain all the distributions of life, and he set to work exploring other possible means of dispersal. Darwin demonstrated, for example, that many seeds could germinate after passing through the digestive system of birds and after long spells of immersion in salt water. He also speculated about the dispersal of seeds in earth stuck to the feet of birds, and about animals rafting on current-borne debris or even on icebergs in colder latitudes (1996, Chapters 11–12).

With regard to life, islands can be described as partially open systems. They may be shaped and defined by the sea surrounding them, but the very premise of island life is the occasional breaching of this boundary. Darwin recognized that though the challenges could be extreme, the populating of islands is not fundamentally different from the dispersion of living things anywhere else. Across the planet, the play between geographical openness and closure, the alternation between connectivity and isolation, is working its effects on living things.

In Darwin's words, 'barriers of any kind, or obstacles to free migration, are related in a close and important manner to the difference between the productions of various regions' (1996, p. 281). It is once these barriers are breached — once an organism enters a new environment and cannot easily retrace its steps — that the interesting things start happening. It is not movement or dispersal alone that makes a difference, but the novel interaction with a new environment that this dispersal opens up. As Darwin put it, 'neither migration nor isolation in themselves can do anything. These principles come into play only by bringing organisms into new relations with each other, and...with the surrounding physical conditions' (1996, p. 284).

In a sense, every ecosystem is an island to which plants, animals and other life-forms arrive from other places, from time to time. Real islands, however, offer some of the most clear and striking evidence of the interplay between organisms and new environments: evidence that was to play a vital role in the work of Darwin, Alfred Russel Wallace and other pioneers of evolutionary theory. As Darwin observed on the Galapagos Islands, and Wallace in the Malay Archipelago, island organisms are clearly related to species on the nearest large landmasses — but just as clearly they have their own unique and distinctive features.

This is because, where a group of islands is relatively isolated from the mainland and sufficiently spaced out to make it difficult — but not impossible — for living organisms to travel between islands, they can become a hotbed of evolutionary change. A rare new arrival on an island from the mainland must survive in the new environment and, if it succeeds, its descendents must adapt to the new conditions and opportunities the island provides, becoming in the process a different species. Then if some members from this new species happen to colonize one of the other islands, they will have to adapt again. After a time, the population will be so different that, even if some individuals manage to get back to the original island, they won't be able to interbreed with their relatives. They have become two different species. In a group of islands, this process can be repeated over and over again, as, very occasionally, colonists move between islands, until a whole variety of related species is formed. This kind of relatively rapid formation and spread of new species through a particular geographic region is called **adaptive radiation**.

Darwin's discovery that each of the various species of mockingbirds — or 'mocking-thrushes' as he called them — came from a different island of the Galapagos group gave him the idea of divergence from a common ancestor. This idea was filled out by his research on Galapagos finches, with their different beaks specialized for different kinds of food. The Galapagos finches, like the mockingbirds, were found to vary between islands. Unlike the mockingbirds, however, Darwin also found cases of several different finches inhabiting the same island. What Darwin recognized — not at the time he was collecting his specimens, but much later — was that differentiation between species of finch on the same island was the result of adaptation to different feeding opportunities.

Darwin's work showed how the different opportunities offered by new environments resulted in clear changes in form and behaviour. As with organisms anywhere, island species tend to become specialized for life in a particular environment, slotting into or taking over a particular role or **niche** in the ecosystem. In the Galapagos Islands (Figure 2.6a), the finches have diversified into vacant niches that on the mainland would be occupied by other groups of birds such as woodpeckers and warblers, and their beak shapes have become specialized to handle the particular type of food that they exploit (Figure 2.6b).

Figure 2.6 (a) The Galapagos Islands; (b) some of the Galapagos finches, showing variation in beak shape.

Because of the relative isolation of islands, however, processes of specialization can be especially pronounced. The combination of a restricted habitat and small, isolated populations often gives rise to interesting characteristics. For example, there are often few predators on islands and this can lead to loss of dispersal ability in birds: flying uses a lot of energy and when it isn't necessary for survival, birds do better by becoming flightless, as in the case of the dodo and many other island species.

Further, the fact that islands can often support only small populations means that the range of variation in this population is also likely to be small. If finding an island to wash up on is a lottery, then so too is the sample of genes that the founder population brings with them. Genes contain the basic coding of life, and in sexual reproduction the offspring inherits a composite of genes from both parents. Any rare genes carried by the founder individuals, the sort of 'oddball' genes that would be thinly dispersed amongst large populations, are likely to be passed on and concentrated in a small interbreeding island population. So while some of the unique or exaggerated characteristics of island life are clearly adaptations to prevailing environmental conditions, non-adaptive random effects can also play a part.

2.7 The vulnerability of island life

The evolution of life on small islands, as it is everywhere, is a complex process — and it is often difficult to determine precisely why a population of organisms has evolved in the direction it has taken. The main point to note is that far from being in a state of 'original perfection' when the first representatives of the human species slosh their way onto shore, island ecosystems are an expression of haphazard arrivals, random effects and ongoing selective pressures. Like any ecosystem, an island is less an example of 'Eden', than an open-ended natural experiment.

This is not the same as saying that island ecosystems have no integrity. Far from it. Every ecosystem is comprised of a community of interlocking organisms, each with different roles or functions (this is explored in greater detail in Book 2). Which organisms will take which role is not determined in advance, but there are nonetheless certain vital functions, or niches, which must be filled in every ecosystem.

Island ecosystems demonstrate that there are recognizable patterns in the assembling of biological communities. Population biologists working in the 1960s identified relationships between the number of species found on islands and island size. This led to new understandings of the carrying capacity of areas of land, i.e. the maximum size of population that can survive and maintain itself there, insights that were then transferred to the study of mainland ecosystems (MacArthur and Wilson, 1963).

The work by population biologists also brought experimental and mathematical evidence to something that had been surmised ever since the early human impacts on previously uninhabited islands such as Mauritius. Namely, that island life has a high level of vulnerability in the face of disturbance. Under conditions of rapid transformation, the evidence suggests, island life finds it particularly difficult to adapt.

Activity 2.3 The dodo's demise

Looking back to the dodo's demise, see if can you can pick out the characteristics of *Raphus cucullatus* that contributed to its lack of resilience (aside from its culinary attractions!). Go for four general points that might be relevant to other species in a similar predicament.

Comment

Here's what we came up with:

- endemism (i.e. found in only one place)
- limited range and small population base (i.e. a narrow range of genetic variation)
- loss of dispersal ability (i.e. flightless)
- lack of defensive adaptations (naive behaviour)

Put these factors together and you have a general picture of why island species are particularly vulnerable to changes made in their habitat by humans (and by the other life-forms that humans bring with them). What we are seeing here is that the same barriers that channel island species into novel and unique forms also diminishes their capacity to adapt to 'stressful' situations. By definition, species found in one small place only are rare, and '(t)o be rare is to have a lower threshold of collective catastrophe' (Quammen, 1996, p. 275).

Islands may be hotspots of biological diversity — or **biodiversity** — but they are also places were biodiversity is most under threat. Just as oceanic islands are susceptible to geological activity, island life is relatively vulnerable to extinction. What counts is the time-scale on which we view processes of transformation. Today there are heated debates about 'background' levels of extinction vis-à-vis the rates of human-induced extinction. One thing that no credible observer can dispute, however, is the extremely high rate at which island species have disappeared.

In the past 400 years, the basic elements of the dodo story have been repeated on numerous occasions. Some 171 of the planet's bird species and subspecies are believed to have gone extinct (Figure 2.7): 155 of them (c. 91%) are from small islands.

Figure 2.7 Museum specimens of dodos, surrounded by other extinct birds.

This figure includes 24 species on the Hawaiian Islands and 13 more besides the dodo on Mauritius and the other two islands that comprise the Mascarene Islands. Lord Howe Island, a pinprick of land in the sea between Australia and New Zealand turns out to have lost more bird species than Africa, Asia and Europe combined! (Quammen, 1996, p. 264). All in all, island birds have been about 50 times more likely to become extinct than mainland birds — and some three-quarters of the island extinction has occurred on small islands. The fate of the birds is only a more extreme example of the risks to island life in general.

So as well as teaching us about the origins of new species, islands have also provided most of our knowledge about the extinguishing of life. The majority of this experience of extinction is directly or indirectly related to European maritime expansion around the globe over the last five or six centuries.

- Can you suggest three main anthropogenic causes of species extinction?
- Three possibilities are:
  - over-exploitation, e.g. hunting or harvesting
  - habitat damage, e.g. deforestation
  - bioinvasion

On islands, each of these human-induced factors exacerbates an already present vulnerability. Direct exploitation of species diminishes the numbers of the already rare, habitat destruction increases internal competition, while the introduction of novel species introduces external competition. What makes the problem of bioinvasion particularly deadly is that the type of organism introduced often belongs to classes or genera (groups of species) that would never have made it across the ocean without human assistance.

- Can you think of an invasive genus not yet mentioned that has a close association with maritime transport, and a particularly bad reputation for damaging island ecosystems?
- Rats — the genus *Rattus*.

The reason for the high number of extinctions already noted on Lord Howe Island is largely down to rodents. In 1918 a supply ship ran aground and its resident black rats (*Rattus rattus*) got ashore. Within a few years the rats were responsible for the extinction of at least six endemic bird species.

In many other cases the direct cause of extinction is not so clear cut. This is because human impacts rarely work alone. What human-induced disturbance does is weaken the resilience of a species or ecosystem, eroding its adaptive capacity. But the fatal blow may then be one of the quite natural perturbations you saw in the previous chapter: a drought, a cyclone, a volcano or any peak or trough in the normal fluctuations of geoclimatic systems. When this happens, human agents may be left none the wiser over their own contribution.

But colonizers of oceanic islands have learnt from experience — as we have seen. So far we have concentrated on the impact of Europeans on previously uninhabited islands, because this history provides some of the clearest and most recent evidence we have of humans entering a new ecosystem. However, uninhabited islands were exceptional, even 600 years ago. The disastrous impact of early Europeans on oceanic islands — and the fact that some important environmental lessons were learnt from these disasters

— raises some interesting questions. For example, what happens when human settlers have occupied islands for a very long time? Can human social systems and island ecosystems ever adjust fully to one another?

2.8 Island ecosystems and island social systems

When European voyagers first came across inhabited tropical islands, particularly in the Pacific, their initial impression was that islanders were innocent and naive people who lived in blissful harmony with nature.

- Does this view remind you of anything you have already read in this chapter, and can you see a potential problem with this view?
- There is a clear parallel with the early European vision of uninhabited islands as Eden-like. However, like all life on oceanic islands, human beings have to actually get there. Crossing oceans and colonizing new lands does not suggest 'innocence' or 'naivety', it points to high levels of technical skill and social organization.

Europeans during the age of exploration imagined a benevolent creator who deposited Pacific Islanders on their tropical Edens. These islanders were in fact descendants of the pioneers of 'blue water' sailing. There is evidence that the first true 'navigators' (people who could sail beyond the sight of land and still find their way home) set out from the peninsulas and close-packed islands of southeast Asia and the East Indies. Known by anthropologists as 'Austronesians', these people mastered the art of long-distance ocean sailing some 3000–4000 years ago. They went on to discover and colonize nearly every sizeable Pacific island (Figure 2.8), and settled as far away as Madagascar, in the southwest of the Indian Ocean. Descendants of Austronesian

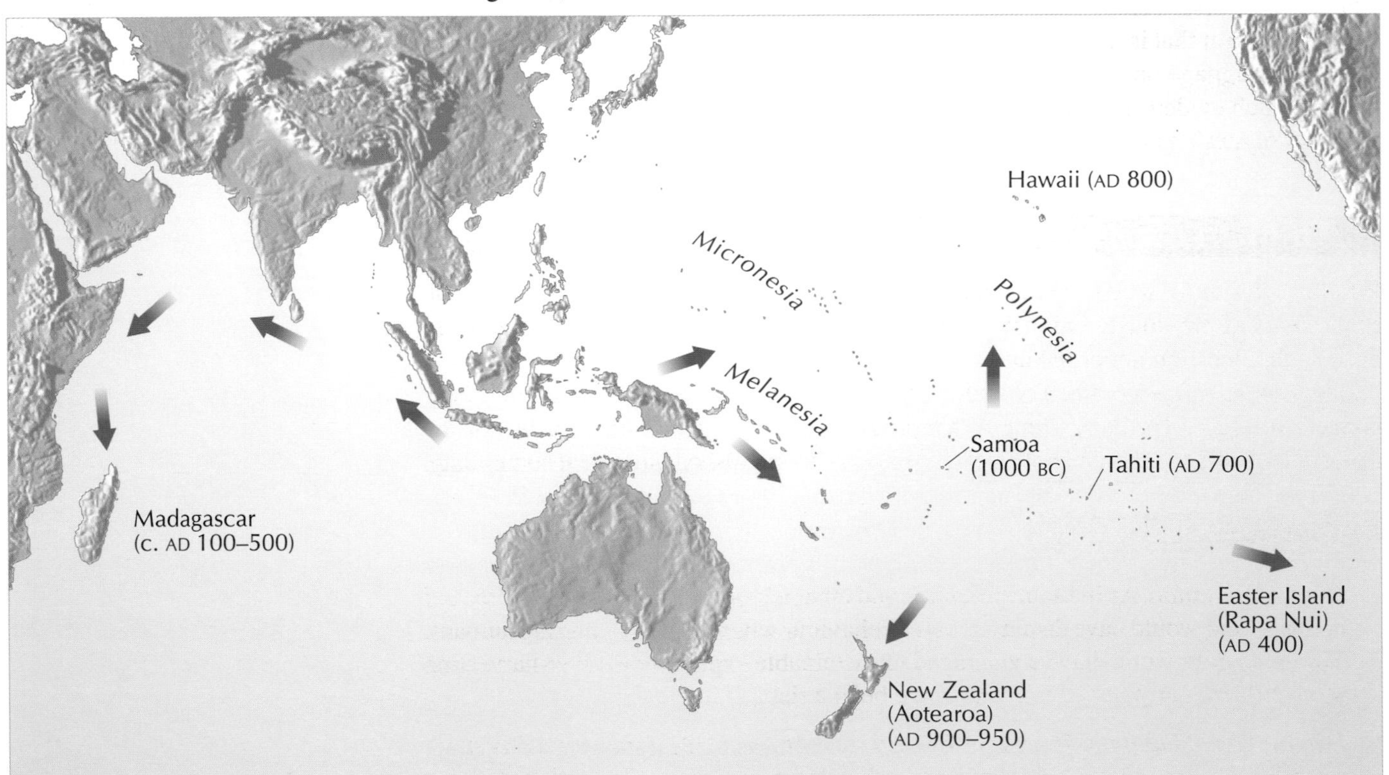

Figure 2.8 A map of the Austronesian diasporas, showing dates of colonization.

navigators still inhabit the islands that their ancestors discovered, and many of these islands are the 'tropical paradises' that westerners love to dream about or visit.

Pacific islands may look pristine to the casual visitor, but all settled lands bear the traces of their inhabitants. One of the transformative forces the first Pacific colonizers brought with them was fire. This was not the occasional fire of the lightning storm or volcano, but a deliberate and regulated anthropogenic burning. Humans have introduced fire almost everywhere they have travelled, using it to clear away old and dense vegetation, and to release nutrients and stimulate new growth. In many cases it is the sudden increase in deposits of charcoal in the geological record of islands that enables archaeologists to date the arrival of the first human colonists (Pyne, 1997).

Humans also brought their own flora and fauna. 'The surprise, indeed the miracle, of Pacific islands', historian Greg Dening notes: ' is how much of what seems natural to rich and easy South Seas living had to be transported' (1992, p. 308). A great many of the fruits and vegetables that fed migrating islanders — such as breadfruit, taro, plantain, even at times, coconut, were transplanted from island to island, as were the trees they used for building and clothing. So too were the pigs, dogs and chickens they feasted on — which all came from the Asian mainland. The small Pacific rat, *Rattus exulans*, almost always came along too. It was probably a stowaway in many cases, but it was also valued as a food source by some Polynesians and so may have been deliberately introduced to many islands.

Figure 2.9 A Polynesian outrigger canoe.

It is the very richness of the biota transported by Pacific Islanders in their canoes (Figure 2.9) that finally convinced western researchers that inter-island migrations were well-planned ventures, rather than accidental, storm-blown occurrences. The long-term viability of the island ecosystems that were at least partly crafted by Pacific seafarers suggests that the species they introduced, and the species endemic to the islands they discovered, have assembled themselves into a functional biological community. But that is not to say that the establishment of humans and all their cultural and biotic baggage on a previously unsettled island was a congenial business. In fact, there is much evidence to suggest that the colonizing of the Pacific by the ancestors of today's Polynesians had serious environmental impacts.

Activity 2.4 Island colonization as an ancient environmental challenge

What do you think would be the likely impacts of a Polynesian colonization on the ecosystems of previously uninhabited Pacific islands? You will find it useful to refer back to the question about the anthropogenic causes of species extinction in Section 2.7. Jot down a few points. Try and expand on your answers to explain why these impacts would be likely to occur — keeping in mind both the characteristics of the new arrivals, and the characteristics of the previously established biological community.

Comment

Over-exploitation. As in Mauritius, birds and other island wildlife would have lacked defences and would have displayed naive behaviour when first encountering humans. This behaviour would have encouraged unsustainable exploitation. Over-harvesting of useful trees or plants might also have been a risk.

Destruction of habitats. The use of fire and other forms of clearance for cultivation, as well as felling of trees for housing and canoe-building, could have had major impacts on the composition of ecosystems and habitats.

Bioinvasion. Pigs, dogs and rats would all have had serious impacts. As you have seen, island fauna — especially flightless and ground-nesting birds — are usually unaccustomed to predatory and scavenging mammals. Some introduced plants might also be expected to proliferate.

You might have noted that although settlers and their accompanying species may be arriving from islands that are no great distance apart, the levels of evolutionary specialization on islands tends to ensure a high degree of differentiation between their species. This means that much of the previous experience of ecosystem exploitation of newly arriving human groups would not be directly transferable to their new home. It should also be kept in mind that some voyages of settlement, such as the colonization of Aotearoa (the Maori name for New Zealand), involved long journeys to very unfamiliar environments. Though the colonization of Aotearoa was clearly successful, there is evidence of numerous bird extinctions. Smaller islands could be even more vulnerable. In the far east of the Pacific, the island of Rapa Nui (the local name for Easter Island) gives us one of the most notorious cases of ecosystem collapse.

Archaeologists now believe that this collapse of Rapa Nui came about primarily through the overexploitation of forests, as a result of the demands arising from the construction and transportation of the monumental stone sculptures the island is now famous for (Figure 2.10). Following loss of vegetative cover and soil erosion came social conflict and population collapse — with a fall from an estimated 10 000 in the 17th century to a few thousand a century later (Bahn and Flenley, 1992). Drought and introduced Polynesian rats may have also played a part, but so too did the closing of contact with other islands inhabited by Polynesians. Loss of timber spelled the end of the construction of large, ocean-going canoes, which precluded the sharing of resources and ideas with other islanders – or any relocation by the people of Rapa Nui.

For all that it is salutary, however, Rapa Nui is an extreme case. Across most of the Pacific the long-term success of Polynesian occupation suggests an eventual coming to terms with the ecological opportunities and challenges of new islands.

Figure 2.10 Monolithic sculpture (*moai*) on the island of Rapa Nui (Easter Island).

2.9 Coevolution of ecosystems and social systems

It is not only human beings who adapt to new conditions. Existing biological communities and incoming species must adjust to each other if both are to survive. Through the process of **coevolution** the different parts of an ecosystem come to fit together through mutual changes that take place over time. Coevolution is not fundamentally different when one of the species in question is *Homo sapiens*, although the challenge can be tough when humans arrive suddenly. You have already encountered a number of situations in which human actions have prompted ecosystems to fall apart or degrade.

In Chapter 1 you saw that the term now used for such misguided interventions is that they are 'unsustainable'. Successful coevolution is thus vital to sustainability. As a generalization, it can be said that human–ecosystem interaction is more sustainable when coevolution between social systems and ecosystems is strong, and less sustainable when coevolution is weak. Not surprisingly, then, Europeans bringing ideas, habits and living things from a distant landmass to a tropical island pose a greater challenge to coevolution and sustainability than islanders on shorter migrations. However, both are at risk of triggering serious changes in the new ecosystems they encounter.

Without a penchant for migration, the human species might well have stayed put in its earliest homeland — the rift valleys of East Africa — and never ventured to all the other regions of the planet. This mobility escalated when the Austronesian people pioneered 'blue water' sailing, and it further accelerated some five or six centuries ago with a wave of European oceanic voyaging. These and other human journeys and migrations were the predecessors of the more encompassing and intensive globalization of the contemporary world.

We have spent time looking at some of these early steps on the way to globalization because they can teach some important lessons. Today, it is often observed that environmental problems such as climate change or pollution overflow the borders of individual countries. This is a significant point, and it has contributed to the way people now think about the world as a single interconnected place. But it is also vital to remember that environmental problems do not just emerge out of modern, developed countries, and flow outwards. What the accounts of early long-distance migrations show us is that environmental disturbance is closely associated with the movement of people beyond the places or regions they were familiar with. In this way, they remind us that environmental problems go back a very long way — well before modern nation states or modern forms of production existed.

Clearly we would not wish to view human mobility in just a negative way — for without migrations and journeys humankind would not have populated most of the planet, and a great deal of the biodiversity of each inhabited part of the world would not be found there. But it is important to keep in mind that wherever there is long-distance movement, there is likely to be an attenuation or break in the coevolution of social systems and ecosystems. There will be high levels of uncertainty in the dealings with the new environment that come from ignorance or lack of experience — and this means that the risk of unsustainable behaviour is greatly heightened. Often, however, people who have migrated long distances do not become aware of the shortfall in their knowledge until disasters occur.

We have seen that the word governance has a root in an old nautical term. It is also interesting to note that the word 'disaster' — which we hear so often today in relation to environmental mishaps — also has a root in navigation. It means, literally, to lose one's star — from the Greek *astron* — meaning star. When you sail far enough that the stars look different, it is time to be very careful!

How humans adapt to new environments in the long term has a biological dimension, like any form of adaptation. But it also has a very strong cultural and social dimension, for it involves learning and social organization. How a group governs itself, or steers its development, plays a major part. Governance is not simply about managing people and their social relations. It is also about managing and directing our relationships with the physical world and the ecosystems that we are part of. How societies govern themselves evolves over time, just as all living things adapt and evolve. As we saw in the case of European island colonies, governance that has a strong element of learning 'from the bottom' has a better chance of nurturing sustainable practices than governance that comes 'from the top' — especially when that 'top' is some place far away.

Where people at the everyday 'grassroots' level are working with, and observing changes in, the environment, they usually have a much better chance of feeding useful ideas and suggestions into the steering of their societies than smaller elite groups whose dealings with the environment are more remote. Governance, in this sense, is a vital part of the coevolutionary processes that lead in the direction of sustainability.

In this chapter, we have seen that the particular conditions of island environments make for both the special creativity and the extreme vulnerability of island life. We have also seen that lessons from islands can be useful for the mainland; islands having worked as a kind of early warning system for environmental problems later faced by the rest of the world. In the following chapter we find out more about physical systems that are variable and turbulent — and how societies cope with them. This will take us away from islands and onto larger landmasses. Here we will pick up on the issue of how societies steer or manage themselves in the face of variability in their environments — and we will look more closely at the question of governance in a global context.

Once you have completed the Questions for Chapter 2 you should go to the Web and finish any activities not yet completed.

2.10 Summary of Chapter 2

2.1 The discovery of uninhabited oceanic islands played an important strategic role in the era of European maritime expansion around the globe.

2.2 The natural endowments and felicitous location of oceanic islands prompted comparisons with the biblical Garden of Eden in the imagination of Europeans.

2.3 The disastrous impact of provisioning stops and settlement on small oceanic islands gave European colonists an early experience of environmental degradation. It was a forerunner of what has come to be called 'unsustainable development'.

2.4 Oceanic islands provided important early lessons about the vulnerability of island wildlife to human impacts, including invasion by introduced animals.

2.5 Settlers and administrators on small island colonies learnt some important lessons about the governance of their societies — and especially about managing their relations with the environment — from their experience of environmental degradation.

2.6 The main legacy of the early European experience of uninhabited oceanic islands has been the idea that the ideal landscape is a 'pristine' one, devoid of any noticeable human alteration.

2.7 The privileging of unspoilt wilderness as the ideal model of nature in the western imagination has had a major impact both on the imagery of both the tourist industry and modern environmentalism.

2.8 Studies of island species gave pioneering evolutionary theorists such as Darwin and Wallace important insights into the processes of diversification of living organisms.

2.9 The same processes that contribute to the peculiar creativity of island environments with regard to biological diversification also render island species especially vulnerable to environmental changes. This has been manifest in high rates of extinction of island fauna.

2.10 Polynesian colonization of oceanic islands seems to have had deleterious effects on island ecosystems in much the same way as European settlement led to severe environmental disturbance on islands.

2.11 Lack of coevolution between human social systems and ecosystems — particularly following human migration — is a significant contributing factor to unsustainable practices.

Learning Outcomes for Chapter 2

When you have completed this chapter, you should be able to:

2.1 Define and use, or recognize definitions and applications of, each of the terms given in **bold** in the text. (Questions 2.1 and 2.5)

2.2 Describe the environmental lessons that can be learned from the experience of European colonization of oceanic islands. (Questions 2.2–2.4)

2.3 Explain how an understanding of island ecosystems challenges the idea of islands as 'Edens' or places of natural 'perfection' (Questions 2.6 and 2.7)

2.4 Explain why islands are both biodiversity hotspots, and places where biodiversity is particularly vulnerable. (Question 2.8)

2.5 Explain the environmental risks of long-distance migration using the concept of coevolution. (Questions 2.9 and 2.10)

Questions for Chapter 2

Question 2.1

Which of the following, if any, are characteristics of ecosystems?

(a) They include interacting organisms and their physical environment.

(b) Each organism belongs to one ecosystem only.

(c) The degree of interconnectivity between its parts gives an ecosystem its distinctiveness.

(d) Ecosystems are open to flows of energy but closed to flows of matter.

(e) Ecosystems and social systems should be treated separately.

Question 2.2

List four useful services that an oceanic island might have offered a 17th-century crew stopping over on a long sea voyage.

Question 2.3

Describe, in a maximum of 70 words, the environmental problems that followed from deforestation of small islands — as identified by early European colonists.

Question 2.4

List four characteristics of the dodo that made it particularly vulnerable to the predatory animals introduced to Mauritius.

Question 2.5

Explain, in two or three sentences, how the notion of 'governance' differs from that of 'government'.

Question 2.6

Put the following in the correct historical order:

(a) The idea of wilderness is established as a mainstay of modern environmentalism and tourism.

(b) European seafarers discover uninhabited islands far out in the ocean.

(c) Uncultivated lands become rare around the European seaboard.

(d) As the development of North America and other 'new worlds' proceeds, people become increasingly nostalgic for uncultivated, undisturbed 'wilderness'.

(e) The idea of undefiled 'Edens' is transferred from uninhabited islands to other newly discovered regions that are already populated.

(f) The idea of islands as pristine undefiled 'Edens' cements itself in the European imagination.

Question 2.7

Which of the following, if any, are characteristics of island ecosystems?

(a) Island species are often clearly related to nearby mainland species.

(b) The organisms that find their way to islands are genetically suited to island life.

(c) Island species may diverge from their mainland relatives in pronounced and unusual ways.

(d) On a cluster of islands, the descendents of a single population of organisms can often be observed to differ from island to island.

(e) How a species evolves on an island is determined by the random cluster of genes carried by its founder population.

Question 2.8

Explain, in two or three sentences, how human disturbance and natural variability can work together as causes of extinction of island species.

Question 2.9

Assess the following statement, in no more than 130 words:

Because they were brought from other Pacific islands, the species introduced by Polynesians slotted comfortably into the ecosystems of newly discovered Pacific islands.

Question 2.10

Which of the following, if any, are correct interpretations of the concept of coevolution?

(a) Humans have only coevolved with the East African ecosystems in which they originated.

(b) Because of their culture and social organization, humans coevolve quickly wherever they go.

(c) Long-distance migration generally makes coevolution between humans and their new ecosystems more difficult to accomplish than shorter moves.

(d) Learning from 'grassroots' experience can assist societies in the process of coevolution with unfamiliar ecosystems.

References

Bahn, P. and Flenley, J. (1992) *Easter Island, Earth Island*. London: Thames and Hudson.

Darwin, C. (1996/1859) *The Origin of Species*, 6th edn. Oxford: Oxford University Press.

Dening, G. (1992) *Mr Bligh's Bad Language: Passion, Power and Theatre on the Bounty*. Cambridge, New York: Cambridge University Press.

Grove, R. H. (1995) *Green Imperialism: Colonial Expansion, Tropical Island Edens and the Origins of Environmentalism 1600–1860*. Cambridge: Cambridge University Press.

MacArthur R. H. and Wilson, E. O. (1963) *The Theory of Island Biogeography*. Princeton, N.J.: Princeton University Press.

Pyne, S. J. (1997) *Vestal Fire*. Seattle and London: University of Washington Press.

Quammen, D. (1996) *The Song of the Dodo: Island Biogeography in an Age of Extinctions*. London. Pimlico.

Rampino, M. and Caldeira, K. (1994) The Goldilocks problem: climatic evolution and long-term habitability of terrestrial planets. *Annual Review of Astronomy and Astrophysics*, **32**, pp. 83–114.

World Resources Institute (2000) *World Resources 2000–2001 People and Ecosystems: The Fraying Web of Life*. Washington D.C.: World Resources Institute.

3 Weathering extremes: the challenge of dynamic systems

Prepared for the course team by Nigel Clark

3.1 Steering through stormy weather

What makes it so difficult to pin down the human contribution to climate change, as we have seen, are the natural fluctuations of geoclimatic systems. All life has to weather these ups and downs, along with occasional upheavals such as fire, disease or geological unrest. One of the implications of this is that human impact on biological communities rarely operates alone. As we learnt from looking at island life, human-induced stress can push a species or community into the danger zone — but the final blow may be delivered by nothing more than the 'ordinary' extremes of environmental variability.

It would be a mistake, however, to let our concern with the vulnerability of living things overwhelm our appreciation of life's achievements. In the face of all the challenges posed by variable conditions and extreme events, life flourishes over most of the planet. Ecosystems endure and thrive, as we saw in Chapter 2, because they can adjust and adapt. And this endurance, of course, also applies to human life — which has prevailed through times of great variability and upheaval.

In this chapter, we engage more closely with the dynamics of physical and living systems, and what they mean for human social life. Some of the changes that living systems go through are extremely hard to predict, and this uncertainty can present enormous challenges to the human groups who depend on them. Starting with marine ecosystems that are vital to many island communities, we move on to the interplay of climate systems and agricultural systems, which operate at much larger scales, and shape the lives of millions of people.

How we live with the uncertainty that is inherent in the physical world is not just a problem of understanding nature, but also a question of organizing ourselves. How can we best steer our societies through rough patches? How should we govern ourselves and our activities so as not to be caught off guard by extremes or sudden shifts in the physical systems we depend on?

These are issues that present themselves at every level of human social existence — from the local right up to the global. After reviewing some earlier 'experiments' in governing social systems on a major scale, this chapter opens up the question of global governance, in the context of the many forms of connectivity that now appear to bind us together across great distances.

3.2 Reef wars: catastrophe and the coral–seaweed competition

Island ecosystems, as you have seen, are particularly sensitive to environmental change. While we concentrated on land-based birds in the last chapter, terrestrial species are not necessarily the top priority of the people who live on islands and atolls.

Figure 3.1 A photograph of coral, sponge and searod.

It is marine life that is often closest to the heart of small island communities. And at the core of the marine ecosystem, in tropical oceans, is the coral reef. In terms of their biodiversity, coral reef ecosystems have often been compared to tropical rainforests.

Coral creates its own substrate, as the skeletons of the coral polyp gradually build up over the years into structures of considerable size (Figure 3.1). Not only are entire islands composed of coral (Figure 3.2), but encircling reefs also protect islands from the eroding effects of wind and wave. Without this 'barrier' effect, it would be difficult or impossible for many islands to build up functioning terrestrial ecosystems.

For a great many generations, island and coastal people have harvested the rich marine life on and around coral reefs. More recently, coral reefs have emerged as a major draw-card for tourists, as the Maldivians well know. But popular appreciation of the coral ecosystem has a dark side. Since the 1980s, evidence from the Pacific and Indian Oceans and the Caribbean has been building into a real fear over the future of coral reefs and the people who depend on them. As was suggested in the articles on the Maldives in Chapter 1, this concern is linked with global climate change.

The problem stems from the fact that coral can only live in water within a narrow temperature range: approximately 25–29 °C. What happens when the threshold is crossed is that there is a disturbance in the relationship between corals and the microscopic algae called zooxanthellae that live within them. Zooxanthellae give coral the rich coloration they are renowned for, but more importantly, they provide them with nutrients through photosynthesis.

Rising temperature stresses the coral, and they expel their zooxanthellae, turning white or 'bleaching' as a result. Bleached coral may recover after a short period of slight warming, but a temperature rise for more than six months is likely to prove fatal. Whole reefs are now said to be endangered, with implications for all levels of the tropical marine ecosystem.

In this way, the degradation of coral reefs has emerged as one of the key symptoms of global warming, adding new weight to the idea that islands are the planet's environmental early warning systems.

Figure 3.2 The coral island of Ambergris Cay, Belize.

But there is more to the problem than this. The dynamics of the coral reef ecosystem are not a simple case of growing human impact leading to mounting coral mortality. Instead, there are surprises in store, and the nature of these 'surprises' has some rather important lessons for our understanding of ecosystem dynamics.

For a start, there are more variables affecting coral than just temperature. One of the main factors is the part played by coral's main competitor — fleshy macroalgae — otherwise known as seaweed. When coral are weak and distressed, macroalgae have a tendency to move in, smothering the reefs and establishing their own 'regime'.

In this play-off between two potentially dominant forms of reef life, a number of variables can tip the balance. Storm damage can work against coral. So too can a decrease in the population of the fish species that graze on seaweed and keep it in check. Or an increase in the nutrient loading of the water, which can cause the zooxanthellae to grow too large or too fast — harming the coral.

Each of these factors occurs naturally, and each can work in combination with temperature-induced bleaching. Each of them, as you may have noticed, can also have a human component.

- Along with anthropogenic global warming, what other human impacts do you think might contribute to the advance of macroalgae at the expense of coral?

- Anthropogenic climate change could be increasing storm frequency and severity. Sewage and agricultural runoff contributes to nutrient loading. Over-fishing removes a check on macroalgae.

Human damage to coral reefs can also be more direct, as in the case of destruction for coastal development, anchor damage or souvenir taking. Add this to the over-fishing and sewage problem, and we are back with the trade-off between development and sustainability that you read about in Chapter 1. Clearly, global scale climate change is not the only issue. The pressure of human numbers on a tropical island can also jeopardize the very attractions that bring visitors: a big dilemma for islands dependent on tourist revenue (Figure 3.3).

Figure 3.3 Coral reefs have become a major tourist attraction.

In this light, we might expect islanders to keep a very close watch on the tug-of-war between coral and macroalgae, and to use this information as an indicator of stress on the ecosystem. However, it is not quite so simple. As it turns out, the amount of coral and macroalgae present may not be a particularly useful sign of the health of the coral ecosystem.

It comes down to the dynamics of the reef ecosystem. The coral regime and the macroalgal regime are **alternative stable states** of the reef ecosystem. At any moment, either 'regime' is likely to be dominant, but the system is much less likely to be found in any intermediate state where coral and macroalgae are co-present. Once a certain threshold of stress has been crossed, the switch between coral and macroalgae tends to be quite sudden (Scheffer et al., 2001).

Does this situation sound familiar? In Chapter 1, you encountered a climatic system that had the potential of rapidly switching between two 'states' or 'phases'.

- Can you recall the massive land-form that was at risk of such a shift, and the term given to this sort of event?

- The land-form was the West Antarctic Ice-Sheet and the process is known as a 'catastrophic shift' in a system.

As we suggested in Chapter 1, many natural systems are vulnerable to catastrophic shifts between stable states. And though no state is more 'natural' than its flip side, the level of biodiversity supported by one state often far outweighs the other, making it vastly preferable to humans. Just as coral reefs are biologically richer than seaweed-smothered reefs (Figure 3.4), so too are clear lakes richer than lakes clouded with phytoplankton, and vegetated lands more life-supporting than parched deserts.

An example of a change in state that seriously affects many people around the North Atlantic is the collapse of the cod population (Box 3.1). This example illustrates well the way that events referred to as 'catastrophic' in scientific terms can also be experienced as 'catastrophes' in the everyday sense of the word. However, we should not assume that *all* catastrophic events are detrimental to humans.

Box 3.1 Alternative stable states: has cod had its chips?

The coastal waters of the North Atlantic, around Newfoundland, were once alive with Atlantic cod (*Gadus morhua*) that occurred in legendary abundance. Huge quantities of fish were taken from these grounds in the 19th and 20th centuries. When fears were expressed that the stocks might become exhausted, the highly influential zoologist Thomas Henry Huxley responded that 'Any tendency to over-fishing will meet with its natural check in the diminution of supply…'. These words, delivered to an international gathering on fisheries in 1883, gave scientific credence to the notion that over-fishing could not occur and that the seas offer a limitless bounty of food (Kurlansky, 1999). This view is still common today, though there is now plenty of evidence to the contrary.

When cod stocks in Newfoundland waters crashed in the 1980s, it was thought that they would recover, as they had done a century earlier when another decline had occurred. A moratorium on cod fishing was introduced by the Canadian government in the 1990s, and scientists and fishers began to wait for stocks to recover. It now appears that they may wait in vain. Other over-fished stock, such as herring in the North Sea, appear to be able to recover when fishing is reduced. Could cod be different? No certain answer can be given to this question, but there is a plausible theory that the marine ecosystem that supports cod fisheries has two alternative stable states, one with cod in tremendous abundance and one with very low numbers. If this is true, cod populations may never recover.

The key to this theory lies in the ecology of cod. It is a large, predatory fish that feeds upon smaller predatory species of fish. The prey of the smaller predatory species include the fry of the cod. So long as large cod are present in abundance, populations of the smaller predators are held in check by predation and this permits sufficient cod fry to escape to maintain a healthy population of cod. However, when adult cod numbers are drastically reduced, fewer small predators get eaten and their population rises. A higher population of small predatory fish means that fewer cod fry escape predation and so the population of adult cod cannot increase. Cod are locked into permanently low abundance (Pauly et al., 2002).

Our growing knowledge of the susceptibility of many ecosystems to catastrophic shifts has enormous implications for the way we engage with environmental issues. Along with much of western science, the study of environmental problems has tended to seek out simple cause-and-effect relationships. We are still more used to thinking in terms of changing conditions that give rise to corresponding changes in natural systems in a

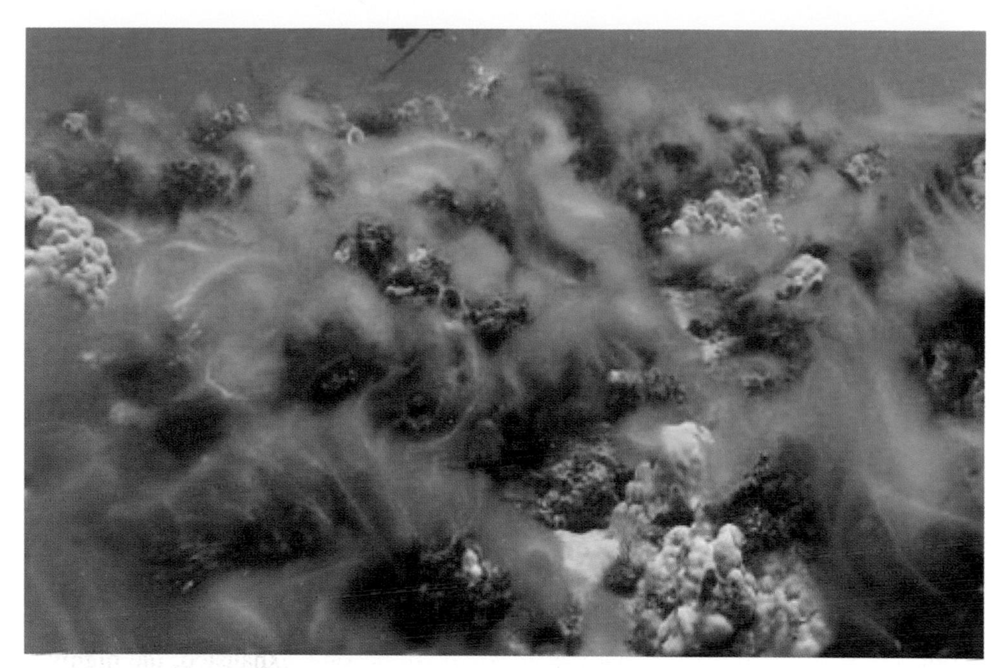

Figure 3.4 A coral reef being smothered by macroalgae.

gradual, or incremental way (recall the ball-bearing rolling along a flat surface in Box 1.1).

If we assume change is incremental, we can also assume that there is an opportunity to step back and reassess what we are doing if our impacts on a natural system seem too severe.

But the potential for catastrophic shifts challenges this assumption, because of the suddenness of the shift between states (the ball-bearing dropping off the table). Once the shift becomes apparent, it is generally too late to stop it. And once it is over, it can be extremely difficult to reverse it and return to the old state or regime. In the case of the coral reef, for example, the heavy presence of macroalgae prevents the resettlement of coral larvae, even when these larvae are plentiful.

3.2.1 Tangling with complex systems

How is it that an ecosystem can transform so suddenly — even when the conditions that promote such a shift may be changing only gradually?

There is no easy answer, but the capacity for this sort of transformation has a lot to do with the complexity of living systems. What defines an ecosystem, as we saw in the last chapter, is the degree of interconnectivity between its parts. Ecosystems and other biological systems (including social systems) belong to the category of **complex systems**, which means not only that they have many components, but that they have many connections between these components and with the world beyond the system itself.

It is the richness of these connections that gives complex systems properties not found in less 'well-connected' systems. Most importantly, complex systems are dynamic or adaptive: they can change over time in response to changing conditions. What makes this possible are the loops in the internal connections of the system, which means that the effects of an activity can pass through a chain of connections and feed back into the system.

Through many 'iterations' or cycles of **feedback**, a complex system is able to reorganize its parts and their connections, developing new pathways or ways of doing things. Less complex systems, such as snowflakes or stereos, may have many parts, but they lack the loops of interconnectivity that enable such adjustments.

In the case of biological systems, this capacity for adjustment is clearly a rather momentous quality, for it allows living things to both maintain their integrity in the face of changing conditions and, under certain circumstances, to transform themselves.

Feedback loops can dampen down the effects of change to help a system stay stable, just like our helmsman in the previous chapter, who keeps the ship on course. This is termed **negative feedback**. It is what takes place when living coral adjusts to small changes in ocean temperature and succeeds in keeping its internal state within the limits needed for survival.

But feedback can also amplify the effects of change, as in cases where a response of the system to change promotes further change. This sort of self-reinforcing cycle of effects is termed **positive feedback**. This is what happens, for example, when a population grows rapidly, with new members of the population adding to the potential for further growth. Positive feedback opens up the possibility of major transformations in the state of a system.

In the case of coral ecosystems, both forms of feedback are occurring. Up to a point, negative feedback keeps the coral regime stable, but once stress pushes the coral past its tolerance levels, change-inducing positive feedback rapidly takes over: macroalgae proliferate and coral dies off.

From the human point of view, the real challenge is working out the current state of a system: where it's at, and what it's likely to do next.

- Thinking back to Chapter 1, can you recall why it is difficult to predict if or when a catastrophic shift in a system is imminent?

- Systems typically lack recognizable warning signals that a change is coming.

Warning signs may be present, but the trouble is that they tend to be beyond our comprehension. To the observer, the ecosystem looks to be stable and healthy, despite the fact that it may be approaching a threshold.

So, if the observable state of a complex living system does not give us enough clues as to its current state, is there any other way of finding out?

These days computers offer a window into the dynamics of complex systems. They do this by enabling us to construct and run a 'model' of the system. This process entails writing down a mathematical relationship (equation) for each of the links within the ecosystem. These equations will show how we expect one part of an ecosystem to change if we alter another component.

However, as you will see, even computer modelling cannot render complex systems fully transparent and predictable.

3.2.2 Computer modelling of complex systems

When we construct a computer model we are attempting to simplify a very complex natural system. As you may have noted, this process inevitably reduces some of the complexity that makes a complex system what it is, but it is currently our best shot.

- Can you think of a prediction made by a computer model that most of us encounter on a daily basis?
- Weather forecasts are made with computer models.

This example suggests that we *can* recreate a complex system in a computer, although anyone with experience of weather forecasting will tell you that these models are not always correct! So why *are* computer models sometimes not correct?

Recall the characteristics of a complex system: its richness of internal and external links. If we want to model the coral ecosystem correctly we must understand, for example, how much coral will die if we added, say one 'unit' of macroalgae. To determine this effect we need to do the experiment. This could mean a laboratory or field experiment with live coral and macroalgae, which would entail killing off the coral with the macroalgae bit by bit, watching the results very carefully. We can then draw a graph of the effect of the macroalgae concentration on the viability of the coral, and could expect it to look something like Figure 3.5.

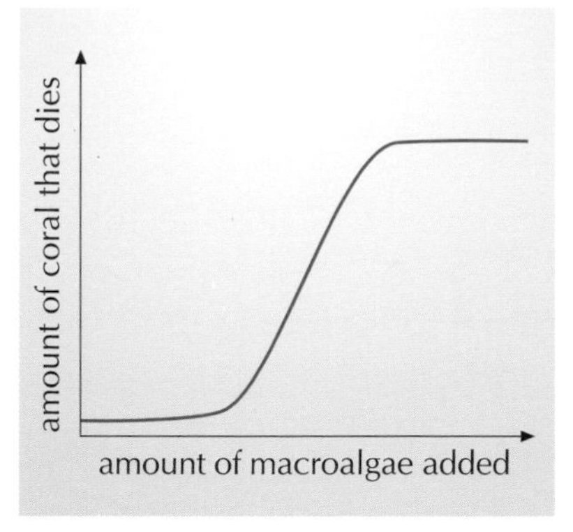

Figure 3.5 A schematic graph of the mortality of coral when macroalgae is added to the system.

You can see in Figure 3.5 that when we start to add the macroalgae to the system not very much coral dies at first. Then all of a sudden the coral dies very rapidly.

Now that we have a graph, we can write down an equation that will say what we think will happen if we add any amount of algae. An equation to describe what is happening in Figure 3.5 is fairly straightforward. However, the difficulty is that we have an equation for just one component of a complex system.

- Can you recall three other components of the coral ecosystem that may change the shape of the graph in Figure 3.5?
- Temperature, nutrient loading and decline in grazers of macroalgae (fish).

Each of these three components will affect the shape of the graph, but we don't know how much they will affect it. What makes it difficult to work this out is the many different ways that these components can interact with each other. We are not just dealing with one form of feedback, but with multiple, entangled feedbacks. It is the multiplicity of feedbacks that can turn a simple graph with a predictable relationship between coral and macroalgae numbers into a graph with an unpredictable catastrophic shift.

So, although we can experiment on one component of a system to see what happens, it is much harder to experiment on a system with multiple feedbacks — which are very difficult to separate and untangle. In other words, what makes a complex system dynamic and flexible also makes it hard to understand.

By using a computer we can vary the equations that link the components and feedbacks to gain a better understanding of how the system will change, including how the feedbacks will change. For the weather you can get a very good forecast of what is going to happen tomorrow. But would you trust a weather forecast for a day two months in the future? We doubt it very much! If we understood *all* the components, and *all* the feedback loops then it should be possible (for a brilliant mathematician) to predict the weather or the state of a coral ecosystem at any time in the future. In the real world, however, there will always be some components and feedbacks that we miss or inadequately account for — and these can make all the difference. This means that while our current models are very good for some situations, they are not so good for pinpointing the moment at which catastrophic shifts are going to occur in complex systems.

For all its limits, however, computer modelling has had a tremendous effect on our society and the way we view the future, as you will see in Book 3.

3.3 Sustainability and ecosystem dynamics

The daunting challenge of anticipating what complex dynamic systems are going to do next means that wherever there is complexity in the world — from the human point of view — there is also uncertainty. And all living systems are complex. So what does this mean for human communities whose livelihoods rely on their local ecosystems? What does it mean, more generally, for our current quest of sustainability?

Arguably, early discussions of sustainability did not give enough attention to the variability of natural systems. But more recent work suggests growing sensitivity towards the dynamic qualities of the natural world, as evidenced by the way the World Resources Institute (WRI) frames the issue of sustainability. In its words:

> The challenge for the 21st century is to understand the vulnerabilities and resilience of ecosystems so that we can find ways to reconcile the demands of human development with the tolerances of nature.
>
> (World Resources Institute, 2000, p. 40)

By **resilience**, what is meant is the capacity of a system to maintain its state in the face of stress or shock. **Vulnerability** is the flipside of resilience, referring to the likelihood that stress or disturbance will fundamentally alter the system.

You should now have a sense of the immensity of the challenge that the WRI is setting out. As we have seen, the difficulty of predicting when systems will change implies that vulnerability and resilience are not readily observable qualities. They are properties of a system that emerge out of many tangled and iterated loops of effects, in ways that no simple 'snapshot' of the system is going to reveal.

These loops or feedbacks stretch through time — sometimes quite significant amounts of time. And this can make it very difficult to link our activities to the undermining of natural resilience.

- From what you read about island ecosystems in Chapter 2, can you explain why there may be time lags between human interventions and their repercussions on ecosystems?
- The lowering of resilience of the ecosystem may only become apparent during extremes of environmental variability.

Figure 3.6 Hurricane waves striking the coast of an island.

In the case of coral, nutrient loading or over-fishing may have reduced the resilience of the ecosystem, but this might not be revealed until a hurricane (Figure 3.6) or heatwave provides the final blow.

What the study of ecosystem dynamics suggests is that the best way to look after ecosystems we value is not to try and prevent all disturbance, but to minimize human impacts that undermine resilience.

The main source of resilience in an ecosystem is **redundancy** — the back-ups, 'spare parts' or alternative pathways that are available in the system. In simple systems, for example most human-built machines, each component is committed to a specific task.

But in living systems and other complex dynamic systems, as you have seen, there is a certain flexibility that allows for adaptability or adjustment. What makes this possible is redundancy.

A high level of redundancy gives a system a kind of uncommitted potentiality for change — so it can absorb stress or shocks without major changes of state. In ecosystems, this usually takes the form of duplication and diversification of function — such as the presence of species with overlapping ecological roles or niches.

- With this in mind, why do you think island ecosystems have been especially vulnerable to human impact?

- The challenge of colonizing islands and surviving on restricted areas tends to result in a high degree of specialization. This is another way of saying that island ecosystems tend to have a relatively low level of redundancy.

3.3.1 Learning how to harvest ecosystems

As we saw in Chapter 2, when human groups colonize a new territory they often view its biological communities as 'bounty' for unrestrained harvest. Until there is experience of the level of exploitation that an ecosystem can tolerate, destructive impacts are likely to continue. But colonists need also to sample the variability and fluctuation in the ecosystems they are dependent on, for the maximum sustainable harvest or yield in a 'good' season may be very different from that in a 'bad' season.

Generally, the longer a social group inhabits a region, the greater the range of variability they will have experienced — including the variability their own activities have induced or amplified. This suggests that those human groups who have successfully occupied an area for a great many generations — people who are often termed 'indigenous — have learnt to weather the extremes as well as the moderate phases of 'their' physical and ecological systems.

We can think of this learning process as a kind of feedback, with human beings in the loop. In cases where change is gradual or steady, this feedback is like that of the helmsman who plays the role of the 'governor' in the system, responding in an ongoing way to changes that can be seen or felt. But in most cases, as you have seen, the complexity of ecosystems means that human activity is caught up in a multitude of mutually entangled feedback loops, which makes for much more indirect and uncertain relationships between human communities and ecosystems.

For most of the span of human evolution this uncertainty was negotiated by leaving ecosystems largely intact. As **hunters and gatherers** (Figure 3.7), the human role in ecosystems was (and some cases, still is) one of 'tweaking' or tuning rather than

Figure 3.7 Coral reef fishing in the Red Sea, Sudan.

controlling. The fraction of total biological production of the system that was consumed was low: probably somewhere around 0.1% (Marten, 2001, Chapter 3). Today, there are still parts of the world where communities, using knowledge accrued over many generations, collectively manage their 'harvesting' of natural ecosystems in such a way as not to undermine their resilience. The way some island communities 'govern' their use of coral reefs is a good example.

New questions of management arise, however, once **agricultural production** takes root. With the development of agriculture a much higher percentage of biological production is made available for human consumption.

Evidence suggests that the domestication of plants and animals may have begun as a response to a reduction in the resources available from natural ecosystems, caused by a period of drier conditions in the Middle East some 12 000 years ago.

Restructuring an ecosystem so that a relatively high proportion of biological production is channelled to human consumers entails a radical simplification of the living system. Humans attempt to cut out those species that compete with them for nutrients ('weeds' or 'vermin'). The result is that in the **agroecosystem** many components and pathways found in the natural ecosystem are no longer present. Henceforth, numerous functions once performed naturally by ecosystems, such as seed sowing, watering and soil fertilizing, have to be taken over by humans (Figure 3.8a, b).

Successive improvements in agricultural technology, such as better water supply, better pest control or higher yield crops, all serve to increase the flow of nutrients to the human part of the system. If this is successful, progressively larger human populations can be supported by a fixed area of land. Historically, this has been the main attraction of agricultural development.

- From what you have learned about ecosystem dynamics, what do you think would be the main drawback of a simplified agroecosystem?

- Because redundancy is lost, the agroecosystem is much less resilient in the face of shocks or stresses than a natural ecosystem.

The more tightly controlled the agroecosystem is, the less humans can rely on the natural working of the system to absorb the effects of climatic extremes — such as drought or heavy rainfall — or upheavals — such as outbreaks of pests or disease. In

(a)

(b)

Figure 3.8 (a) Terraced slopes in Peru. The terracing of hillsides is a long-established agricultural technique that traps and conserves both water and nutrients. (b) Harvesting rice, Guilin, China.

this regard, parts of the Old Testament of the Judaeo-Christian religions can be interpreted as a record of the vulnerability of ancient Middle Eastern agricultural societies to environmental fluctuation and stress.

What this means is that agricultural societies, if they are to survive environmental variability, have to build replacements into the system for the natural redundancy that has been lost. Historically, this has taken many forms — including storing water and stockpiling crop surpluses from good years. It has also involved increasing contact with other societies to gain access to their resources — either through trade or through the more aggressive strategies of plunder and conquest. To put it in contemporary terms, these are the ways that agricultural societies confront the challenge of sustainability.

We talked earlier about the feedback between a hunter–gatherer community and its ecosystem. Picking up on signs about the state of the ecosystem and collectively processing and responding to these indicators is a form of governance: a way that human communities steer and manage themselves, and their relationships with their environment. In an agricultural society, the ecosystem humans rely upon may have been made *less* complex, but this in turn can make the problem of governing the social system rather *more* involved.

This has a lot to do with the extra work that is required to take over functions once performed by natural ecosystems —including the need to cope with fluctuations and shocks once absorbed by these more complex systems. Organizing labour to maintain the agroecosystem, dealing with surpluses and shortfalls, and managing the exchanges with neighbouring societies all create new challenges for governing a society.

Today, the question has arisen about how to steer our societies through the environmental changes that now present themselves at a global scale. This is clearly an immense challenge. However, if we keep in mind that large and complex societies have faced the problem of organizing themselves through environmental extremes and shocks many times in the past, there may be lessons we can learn.

In the following section, we complete our journey away from small islands, and head to the great river valleys of India and China. For thousands of years, the agricultural production of these regions has supported some of the largest and highest density human populations on the planet. But not without some major setbacks.

3.4 Heavy weather: agriculture and climatic variability

The long and gradual development of agroecosystems and the rise of rural populations in India and China share much with traditional or peasant agricultural societies the world over. A common theme in these societies is the alternation between periods of relative comfort, often nostalgically termed 'Golden Ages', and times of great hardship. Hard times can arise out of war and other social unrest, but most often the leading role has been played by environmental adversity.

In southern and eastern Asia, the most important environmental variable is the climatic pattern known as the **monsoon**. By contrast with the temperate regions, with their more evenly spread rainfall, monsoonal regions (Figure 3.9, overleaf) have an extreme seasonal variation in rainfall, with the summer rains providing the vast majority of the years precipitation (75–90% of annual rainfall in India, for example). A so-called good monsoon season is usually one with above average rainfall (Figure 3.10a), while a poor season has a rainfall deficit. Above all, it is 'drought'(Figure 3.10b) — the delay, interruption or absence of the crucial summer rains — that is the major environmental threat for monsoonal Asia.

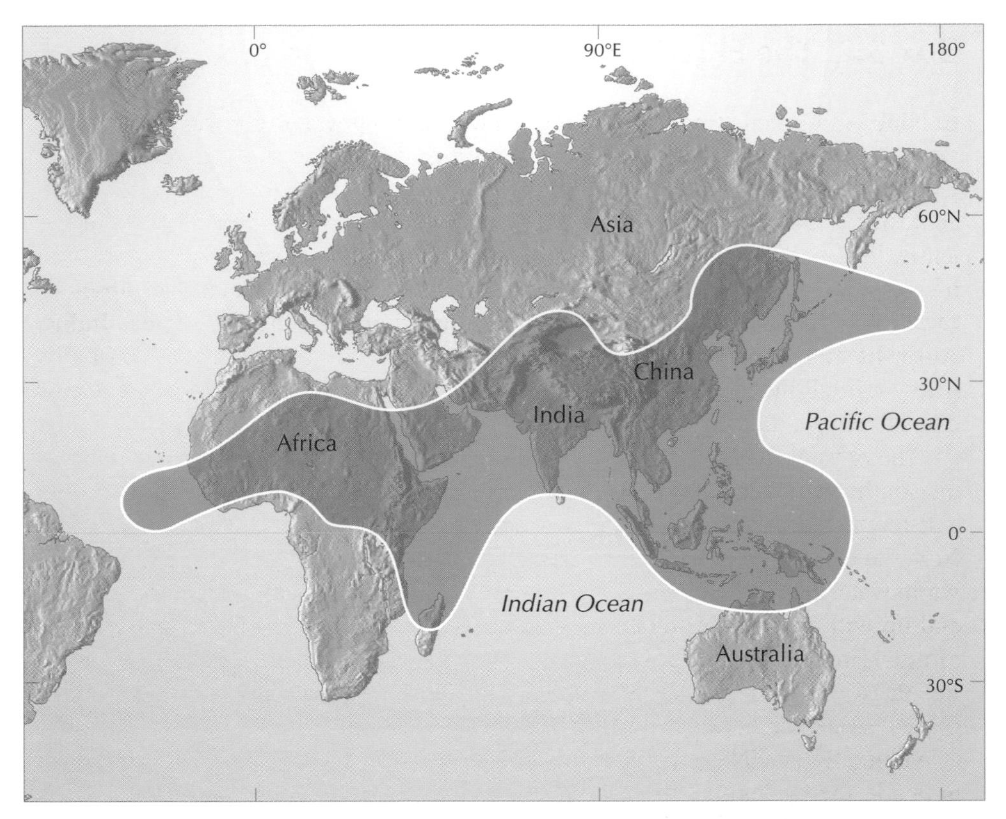

Figure 3.9 Regions affected by monsoon climates in the Eastern Hemisphere.

It is now well understood that behind the refrain of 'golden' and gloomy years are patterns of climatic fluctuation, with long-term records showing distinct phases of above and below average monsoonal rainfall. What recent research suggests, however, is that the rhythms of monsoonal variation do not work alone. Over the last few decades, climate scientists have begun to decipher the workings of another cycle of climatic

(a)

(b)

Figure 3.10 (a) Monsoon rains. (b) The impact of drought on the soil surface.

variability with even wider influence than the fluctuations of the monsoon. This phenomenon is known as the **El Niño Southern Oscillation,** and its effects on global climate are staggering (Box 3.2).

Box 3.2 The El Niño Southern Oscillation (ENSO)

El Niño got its name from South America where it appears on the western coast as very warm surface water within a few months of Christmas — it refers to the Christ Child, or more literally 'The Boy'. The South Americans had known for centuries of the phenomenon but it was only in 1972 — the 'year of the climate anomalies' — that much of the rest of the world really took notice. A massive pool of warm water appeared off the South American coast and caused an upset in rainfall across the globe. There were devastating droughts in Africa, India, Australia and the former Soviet Union. At the same time there was abnormally heavy rainfall in the Mediterranean and along the South American coast, causing extensive flooding.

The physical cause for this natural event is a change in the pattern of winds in the southwestern Pacific Ocean, which allows warm water to effectively slop into a different part of the ocean. Because the water cycle is dependent on evaporation from the ocean, and evaporation is dependent on the temperature of the water, this warm water alters the amount of moisture the clouds can pick up. Sometimes clouds end up with much more moisture than usual, sometimes much less. When these clouds finally rain, people in Asia feel the effect of climate variation in the Pacific. The term given to these couplings of weather events in distant places is **teleconnection**.

Generally an ENSO happens every 2–8 years, although it is very difficult to untangle the cycles that drive it. When it does make an appearance, the ENSO effect can be of greatly varying magnitude. The ENSO of 1972 was a major one.

The cycle of the Asian monsoon, evidence suggests, is not fundamentally controlled by ENSO. But monsoons can be modified by ENSO, and in a rather momentous way. When the monsoon cycle and ENSO are phase-locked — which is to say, when their respective peaks and troughs overlap — then adverse years can turn into very bad years indeed, with extremes of drought and flooding. In this light, it now appears that some of the worst famines in Asian history have occurred at times of monsoonal **phase-locking** with ENSO.

In the years between 1870 and 1990 there were 11 occurrences of very strong ENSO episodes: 1877, 1884, 1891, 1899, 1911, 1918, 1925, 1941, 1957, 1972 and 1982. In the case of India, the strong ENSOs of 1884, 1891, 1941 and 1957 did not result in severe deficits of rainfall. However, the years 1877, 1899, 1918 and 1972 were the worst years of drought recorded over this period (Figure 3.11, overleaf). It was only in these four years, the evidence suggests, that ENSO was phase-locked with a period of rainfall deficit in the Asian monsoon cycle (Kripalani and Kulkarni, 1997).

But does this mean that the monsoonal lands of India and China are destined to disaster and poverty as a result of their unstable climates? Over the last century and a half, this argument has often been put forward by observers in wealthier, temperate countries, in order to explain the difference in living standards between 'tropical backwaters' and their own 'green and pleasant lands'.

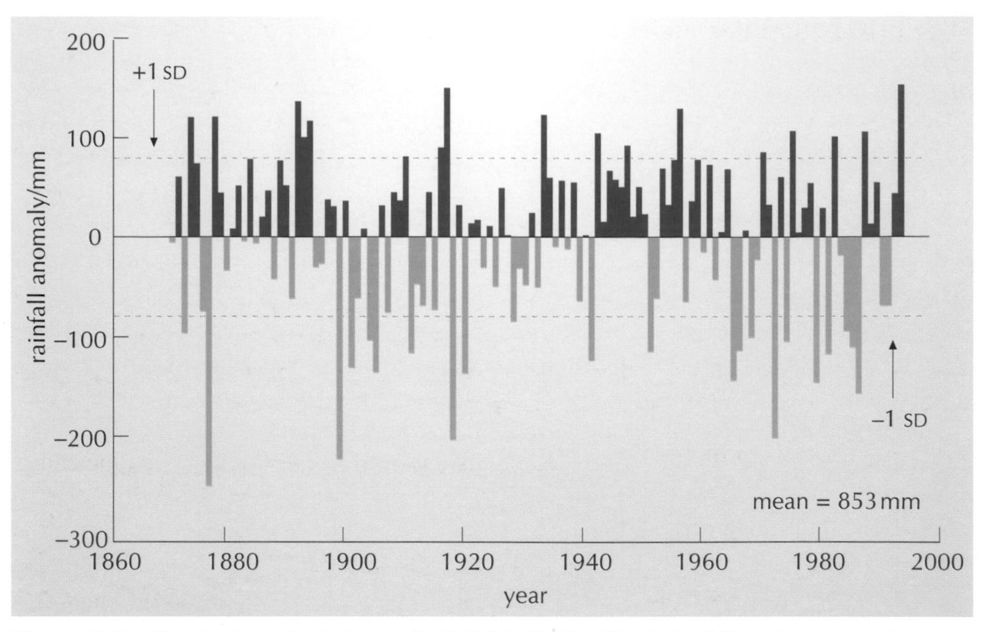

Figure 3.11 Graph of the deviations of rainfall in India. The dashed lines indicate ± 1 standard deviation (SD) from the mean (853 mm).

Clearly, there is a lot more at stake. While advances in the study of climate dynamics have been taking place, researchers have not forgotten other factors that have also shaped the life chances of people in the agricultural societies of India, China and elsewhere. What we are now seeing are some rather interesting attempts to combine new scientific understandings of weather and its effects with the kind of insights into the organization of social life that social science can provide.

One of the questions of growing interest to researchers is how different societies have managed or steered themselves through good, bad and uncertain weather. As we saw above, this is a challenge that every agricultural society has faced.

By the 18th century, it has been argued, imperial China had a system of famine prevention and relief that operated from the state level downwards (Davis, 2001). In times of deficit, food held in provincial granaries was distributed to peasants in officially designated disaster areas, tax breaks were offered, and price controls were put in place to prevent speculation on foodstuffs. In better times, there was extensive state-organized work on infrastructure — such as improving irrigation and waterborne transportation.

Similar measures were taken in pre-colonial India. Though the centralized power of the imperial state did not match that of China, there are records of state level embargoes on food exports, widespread tax concessions and distribution of free food, as well as subsidies for well maintenance and irrigation work. There was also a tradition of maintaining common lands, which were accessible to the poor.

We might see these strategies as a kind of negative feedback in the agricultural social system: a form of response aimed at ameliorating the worst effects of environmental variability in order to maintain stability in the system. As a result of such measures, it has been claimed, even during a phase-locking of ENSO and monsoonal deficit in the mid-18th century, widespread starvation was avoided (Davis, 2001).

Clearly, famine prevention and relief measures are preferable to no measures. However, there are also good reasons to be sceptical of the overall effectiveness of these strategies, as we will see.

3.4.1 Colonial catastrophes: the great famines

Just as the Asian monsoon and ENSO came into phase in the mid-18th century, so too were there episodes of phase-locking in the late 19th century. As we saw above, these were centred on the years 1877 and 1899 (Figure 3.11), and they seem to have been even more pronounced than the 18th-century episode. This, however, may not be the most crucial difference.

By the latter part of the 19th century, much of India had been incorporated in the British Empire and was administered by British officials (Figure 3.12) working in tandem with a powerful local elite. Though China was not politically annexed, European economic influence was strong there also. The implications of this change for the steering of these societies through a phase of climatic extremes, recent research suggests, was profound.

Figure 3.12 Lord Lytton, the Viceroy of India during the 1870s.

Now read the three excerpts from *Late Victorian Holocausts* by social historian Mike Davis in the *Offprints* booklet. Davis describes the response by the British administration to the 1876–9 famine in India and China. There is more detail provided than you require, but aim to get the gist of the argument.

Activity 3.1 The great famines: coping (or not coping) with crisis

Recapping on what you read in the previous section, list five measures taken in precolonial India or late imperial China to prepare for and deal with drought.

Answer

- stabilization of the prices of foodstuffs
- relief operations using stockpiled grains and other food reserves
- tax concessions
- state-subsidized maintenance of waterways, irrigation and flood control
- common land accessible to the poor

From the excerpt from *Late Victorian Holocausts*, see if you can make a comparative list of the ways that British colonial administrators confronted drought.

Answer

- no food relief without forced labour
- price of grain fixed by the 'free market'
- surplus and available food committed to the export market
- no tax relief
- privatization and sale of common land

As we will see, there are good reasons to be cautious about the effectiveness of pre-colonial measures for dealing with climatic uncertainty (as indeed, Davis gives us some clues in the readings). Nevertheless, the evidence put forward by Davis suggests that the famines of the late 19th century were disasters without precedent. The human toll of these two catastrophes in India and China has been estimated at between 30 and 60 million dead.

In many respects, what Davis presents to us here is the gut-level experience of unsustainability in action. In keeping with what we have learnt about catastrophic shifts, his account can be taken as a warning that the symptoms of unsustainability may not simply reveal themselves, step by step. Instead, they can irrupt, rapidly and disastrously.

With this in mind, do you think the human and ecological disasters of the scale Davis has described might reappear? Jot down your immediate impressions.

Comment

There is no simple answer. But our growing knowledge of the possibility of major fluctuations in climate, and catastrophic shifts like the collapse of the West Antarctic Ice-Sheet suggest we should take the question very seriously. You may want to revisit your responses to this question after reading the final sections of this chapter, and again at later points in the course.

So, what can we learn from the tragic famines of the late 19th century? What were their causes and how can we avoid their repetition?

The message of Davis's book is that environmental variation alone cannot explain the magnitude of the 'great famines' of India and China. We must look to other variables too.

In the latter half of the 19th century, Davis points out, India, China and many other agricultural economies were being incorporated into an emerging global economy.

Instead of producing predominantly for local or regional needs, peasant farmers were encouraged, and often compelled (through taxation and other means), to produce for the global market. The result is that prices and conditions of work came to be set by distant market forces.

This led to some boom years in which agricultural production expanded and prices rose. But it also introduced a whole new kind of vulnerability into the social system.

As we have seen at several points in this chapter, the greatest challenges to system stability occur when the extremes of different cycles coincide.

The strength of Davis's interpretation of the great famines is not only that he considers the effects of these physical systems, but that he also takes account of another source of variability: the global economic system. Economic systems, like ecosystems, are complex and dynamic with their own rhythms. As anyone who has ever played the stock market or watched the movement of house prices will know, economies have ups and downs that are notoriously hard to predict. What Davis argues, in the case of great 19th-century famines, is that climatic extremes coincided or phase-locked with a different kind of extreme: world-wide slumps in the global economy.

Newly enmeshed in this economy, and without the traditional reserves and relief to fall back on, peasant farmers across the colonial world were hit at once by economic depression and devastating drought. This meant that downward spirals in prices received for their produce coincided with drastic reductions in their crop harvests. In this way, the extreme effects in the climate system and the extreme events in the economy came together in a self-reinforcing loop: 'a fatal meshing of extreme events' with disastrous implications for the state of the agricultural system. The result was a 'catastrophe' in every sense of the word.

Now would be a good time to go to the Web and do the activities associated with this chapter.

3.4.2 The challenge of governing complex systems

From the problems of preserving coral reefs to the challenge of weathering extremes in agricultural societies seems like a long journey. It should be apparent by now, however, that some similar principles apply. In the dynamics of the coral reef ecosystem, the agricultural society, and the global economy there are multiple, entangled feedbacks, rendering it extremely difficult in each case to predict precisely any future state of the system.

- In the face of such uncertainty, what is the best the way of maintaining the resilience of the system?
- Ensuring there is redundancy or under-utilized potential in the system.

As we have seen, an agroecosystem is one that has been radically simplified by humans, who must then take over responsibility for many of the functions once performed naturally. This includes building in redundancy.

- What were the strategies in pre-colonial Indian and late imperial Chinese systems that might be thought of as building redundancy into the agricultural system?

Figure 3.13 Traditional grain store, India.

- The strategies included stockpiling surpluses (Figure 3.13), storing water in irrigation systems and keeping land in common (assuming the land was not intensively used).

- What do you think the effect of aggressive incorporation into global markets was on these kinds of in-built redundancy?
- Generally, uncommitted potentiality in the system seems to have been converted into productive use, wherever possible. This seems to have contributed in a major way to the vulnerability of these systems to both environmental and economic variability.

Managing the swings between surplus and shortfall by building redundancy into the system, as we saw above, is one of the major challenges of governing an agricultural society. One of the criticisms that can be levelled at the British colonial administrators of India is that their governance, in this regard, was hugely inappropriate.

- Recalling what was said in the previous chapter about the implications of long-distance migration, can you give a reason why the British would have been ill-prepared to govern monsoonal Asia?
- Most of their experience of climate and other environmental conditions came from temperate northwestern Europe — which is beyond the direct sphere of influence of monsoons and the most extreme effects of ENSO.

By this logic, we would expect that governance related to the handling of environmental uncertainty by Indian or Chinese rulers would be much better informed. Although we have seen that 'local' strategies for ameliorating the effects of drought and famine contrasted markedly with colonial tactics, we should be very careful not to give an overly flattering and uncritical picture of pre-colonial governance. There are good reasons to be sceptical of any claims that governance prior to colonial intervention was even-handed or universally effective.

- Recalling what we had to say about 'steering' societies in Chapter 2, how would you sum up the governance that was predominant in pre-colonial India and late imperial China — in a couple of words?
- The evidence we have seen suggests that both the Chinese and Indian administration of drought and famine was heavily 'top down'.

- What do you think the implications of this administration would have been with regard to the needs of 'ordinary' people at ground or grassroots level?
- It should make us doubtful as to whether the interests, knowledge and experiences of people 'on the ground' were taken into full consideration.

While village communities did play a part in managing environmental and economic uncertainty in traditional Asian social life, we need to be mindful of the limits of public participation in decision-making, at the village level, and especially above this level. Economist Amartya Sen (2001) makes the point that traditional agricultural social systems typically fail to offer sufficient economic opportunities or protective arrangements for all members of society. These shortcomings, he suggests, are closely tied to the restrictions on participation at all levels of decision-making. Sen refers to this as 'alienated governance' (Figure 3.14).

Figure 3.14 A painting of Emperor Aurangzeb, the Mughal Emperor of India from 1658 to 1707, being carried by his subjects.

It might be judicious, then, to view the attempts at famine mitigation in pre-colonial India and late imperial China as, at best, patchy and inconsistent. In many cases, the most effective precautions would have been taken at the 'grassroots' level: notably the growing of hardy 'famine crops' like millet or sorghum.

In the case of traditional agricultural societies, China especially, we should also keep in mind that the historical recording of famine mortality — or lack of mortality — has been severely hampered by the incompleteness of data that follows from rural isolation.

However, as we have seen, things could get worse. The problem with British colonial governance was that it was even more alienated from the interests and needs of people 'on the ground'. Moreover, one of the main tasks that European colonial governors set themselves was the opening of peasant or traditional societies to the global market, based on a strong faith that the global market itself is a powerful self-regulating system.

But one of the lessons that might be learned from the tragedies of the colonial period is that markets like many other complex systems, are subject to sudden and surprising shifts. And the effects of these shifts are far from evenly distributed.

Behind this vision of markets as 'self-regulating' is the assumption that they work as a kind of 'level playing field', in which all producers and all consumers have an equal say in 'steering' the system. But this is misleading. Because of the great differences in power and wealth between people who are drawn into markets, the 'playing field' is far from level. Those who have economic resources to fall back on are far more resilient in the face of downturns. Indeed, they can often profit from the vulnerability of smaller producers.

From an environmental point of view, there is a further reason why the level playing field of the global marketplace is a dangerous assumption.

- Keeping the case of monsoonal India and China in mind, can you suggest a reason?
- The extremes of climatic fluctuation and other forms of environmental variability interact with economic variables. This gives an added 'unevenness' to the surface of the global playing field.

In this section, we have focused on climatic fluctuations that affect countries in the monsoonal belt. This should not obscure the fact that vulnerability to climate change is also of vital importance for people living in temperate zones, as you will see in Book 3.

3.5 Global governance: obligations in a connected world

The tension between uneven real world conditions and idealized visions of equality in the global market is no less important in our era than it was over a century ago. Today, to an even greater extent than in the colonial 19th century, there are strong inducements for producers and consumers all around the world to participate fully in global markets.

These markets are highly competitive, putting pressure on producers to bring the maximum amount of produce to the market at the minimum price. Across the world, this pressure is leading to intensification of agriculture and other forms of production (Figure 3.15a, b).

However we choose to conceive of 'development', the sort of economic efficiency that is promoted by competition in global markets must be part of the picture.

As we saw earlier in the chapter, the WRI sees the great challenge now confronting the world as one of understanding the vulnerabilities and resilience of ecosystems in order to reconcile these with the demands of development.

- In the light of the factors that contribute to ecosystem resilience, and the competitive pressures of the global economy, can you see a tension within WRI's challenge?

- Given that redundancy plays an important part in ecosystem resilience, the imperative of protecting ecosystems may pull in a different direction from the demands of development in the global economy. We need to remember that even plans for sustainable development have tended to assume further massive increases in levels of global economic activity (see Section 1.3.2).

The study of agricultural systems brings the issue of resilience and vulnerability in both ecological and economic systems into clear focus. Clearly, we need to take the question a lot further.

Increasingly, over the last two centuries it has not only been agriculture but **industrial production** that has channelled resources towards human consumption. Industry, and industrialized agriculture, takes the process of cutting out 'extraneous' loops and taking over ecosystem functions far further than peasant farmers could ever have imagined. The ultimate aim of industrial production is to place all aspects of the productive system under human control.

For a long time it was thought that the extended control over natural processes implicit in industrial production meant that industrial systems were immune to the vagaries of environmental variability that beset agroecosystems. The rising awareness of global environmental problems over recent decades reveals the flaws in this assumption.

In this chapter we have considered the question of ecosystem resilience and vulnerability at the local scale of the coral reef and at the regional level of the agroecosystem. In a

(a)

(b)

Figure 3.15 (a) Mechanized dredging to clear weeds in the Gezira canals, Sudan; (b) intensive cultivation, Gezira, Sudan.

similar way, we are now impelled to think about resilience and vulnerability at a global scale, as we will see in more detail later in the course.

The quest for sustainability is an attempt to steer the development of our societies on a course that leads away from ecological vulnerability and towards resilience. In this sense, to think about sustainability is to think also about governance: to consider all the processes by which we guide, manage and direct our societies.

Directing communal life in such a way as to keep a local reef healthy and intact, as you saw, is quite a challenge. Administering an entire agricultural society creates a whole new set of demands. And we have seen what can happen when these demands are insufficiently met. Today, we find ourselves having to think about governance at a global level, which presents a challenge of a scale and complexity that is without precedent.

How can we even contemplate steering the social life of an entire planet? One thing we can draw some consolation from is the fact that our understanding of complex systems is advancing steadily. And in many ways the question of governance (which shares its root in *kubernetes* with the word 'cybernetic') is about negotiating complex issues.

Today, it is becoming increasingly apparent that governance that does not involve a high degree of 'feedback' from throughout the social system — from the grassroots upwards — is likely to suffer from serious insufficiencies and imbalances.

This understanding resonates clearly with what we know about the working of complex systems. In particular, we recognize that such systems have properties that emerge out of the interplay of all their elements — properties that cannot, therefore, be found at any single point in the system. No individual, or even a cluster of individuals, by this reasoning, can encompass the interests, the experiences, the learning of all the people who are make up a social system. When we are dealing with any complex system, including a social system, a single 'helmsman' is, quite simply, not up to the task.

Lest this make governance sound like a purely technical problem, it is important to remember the extent of the suffering that can be caused by inappropriate responses to environmental and social change. Our growing understanding of the way that large-scale climatic fluctuation shapes the life chances of people across the globe is a reminder that there are forms of vulnerability that industrial control of the productive process cannot alleviate. This question of vulnerability takes a radical new turn once we acknowledge that industrial activity can actually exacerbate environmental extremes.

The gathering evidence of human-induced global environmental change raises profound issues about our obligations to 'others' distant in time and space. But this sort of ethical issue should not overshadow the possibility that we might also feel obligations toward people elsewhere on the planet who are threatened by quite natural environmental changes. As indeed they might feel responsibility for us.

'Obligation' takes its root from the Latin *ligare*, which means to bind, and there are various ways that our growing sense of ties and linkages to distant others might affect the way we feel obligated to, or responsible for each other, as we will see later in the course.

Just as we are increasingly aware that that the processes of globalization open up new links between people on different sides of the globe, so too does our emerging understanding of the dynamics of global climate suggest that people from different regions are 'teleconnected' in previously unknown ways.

It is this sense of a world made up of intensive connectivity — both natural and anthropogenic — that now impels us to consider the question of governance on a global scale. At the same time, another kind of interconnectivity may also be a condition of any sort of planet-scaled governance. Several centuries ago, shipping networks gave an intimation of global connectivity, by weaving together insights from small islands strung across vast oceans. Today, new information and communication technologies offer novel possibilities for bringing together data and experience from every part of the world.

These possibilities raise an important question. Will these media reinforce top-down modes of control and market-driven pressures — or will they facilitate broad-based 'feedback' and participation in 'steering the globe'? There is no simple answer (at least not from 'inside' the system!) — but it's a question you may wish to reconsider from time to time as you proceed through the course.

3.6 Summary of Chapter 3

3.1 Human impacts can compound the stress caused by natural variability to induce catastrophic shifts in an ecosystem. These shifts often result in a much lower level of biodiversity.

3.2 Ecosystems belong to the category of complex systems, which means they have the potential to stabilize or to transform themselves in response to changing conditions. The tangled feedback loops that enable ecosystems and other complex systems to adjust also make it extremely difficult to predict future states of the system.

3.3 Preserving redundancy tends to be the best means of maintaining resilience in an ecosystem or other complex system.

3.4 Human hunting and gathering communities generally keep their demands on the biological productivity of ecosystems at a low level, which conserves ecosystem resilience.

3.5 The transition to agricultural production involves the channelling of a high proportion of biological production to human consumers and entails a significant simplification of ecosystems. This simplification tends to reduce natural resilience.

3.6 Agricultural societies must find ways to cope with the effects of seasonal and longer-term climatic variability if they are to endure. This means that famine prevention and relief is usually an important aspect of the governance of these societies.

3.7 Integration of traditional agricultural societies into global markets exposes peasant producers to the uncertainties of the global economic system, which can compound the uncertainties of climatic variability.

3.8 Top-down governance has limitations when it comes to responding to environmental and economic variability.

3.9 Because of economic inequality and environmental variability across the planet, there is unevenness to global markets. Global market pressures encourage maximal development of resources, which can undermine resilience in economic and ecological systems.

3.10 Our growing understanding of global interconnections raises ethical questions about our obligations to 'others' distant in time and space, and underscores the need for governance at a global scale. Effective governance requires input and feedback from throughout the social system.

Learning Outcomes for Chapter 3

When you have completed this chapter, you should be able to:

3.1 Define and use, or recognize definitions and applications of, each of the terms given in **bold** in the text. (Question 3.1)

3.2 Describe how the properties of complex systems can affect the behaviour of ecosystems and predict, in general terms, how these properties may influence the sustainability of ecosystem exploitation. (Questions 3.2–3.4, 3.6–3.8)

3.3 Determine how governance can play a role in the behaviour of a complex environmental system. (Questions 3.9 and 3.10)

Questions for Chapter 3

Question 3.1

Which of the following, if any, are characteristics of complex systems?

(a) They are open to inputs from outside the system.

(b) They have many components that are richly interconnected.

(c) They have many internal interconnections but no external connections.

(d) Their feedback loops make them much more stable than simple systems.

(e) They have feedback loops that enable them to adjust under changing conditions.

Question 3.2

An island community that depends upon its coral reefs to attract tourists wishes to develop its tourist industry in a sustainable way. As tourist numbers grow, the islanders monitor the relative areas of their coral reefs that are dominated by coral and dominated by macroalgae. They use the results as the main indicator of the sustainability of their tourist industry developments.

Do you think this is wise strategy? In a maximum of 80 words, explain your answer.

Question 3.3

Which of the following, if any, are reasons why computer models of complex systems have limitations when it comes to predicting catastrophic shifts?

(a) Computer models are simulations that bear no relation to the real world.

(b) Because computers are machines they can only model simple systems without feedbacks.

(c) Computer models can deal with feedback, but it is very difficult to find out what the multiple, entangled forms of feedback are that give rise to catastrophic shifts.

(d) It is very difficult to give values for all components and all feedbacks in the model.

(e) Knowing all components and all feedbacks doesn't help because catastrophic shifts are completely random events and are therefore totally unpredictable.

Question 3.4

Which of the following, if any, are good ways to look after an ecosystem we value?

(a) Minimize the human impacts that undermine resilience.

(b) Prevent all disturbance to the ecosystem.

(c) Reduce redundant aspects of the ecosystem so that it becomes more efficient.

(d) Maintain the diversity of functions and elements in the ecosystem even if they do not appear necessary.

Question 3.5

Which of the following, if any, are ecological implications of the shift from hunting and gathering to agricultural production?

(a) A much higher proportion of biological production is channelled to human beings.

(b) Humans add many new connections and components to the natural ecosystem.

(c) Agricultural technologies take over some the functions once performed by natural ecosystems.

(d) The resilience of natural ecosystems can be severely compromised.

Question 3.6

Which of the following statements, if any, describe the climatic conditions of monsoonal Asia as they are now understood?

(a) The monsoon brings variation in rainfall between seasons and from year to year.

(b) ENSO drives the monsoon system.

(c) The monsoon system drives ENSO.

(d) The main influence of ENSO on the monsoonal system occurs during phase-locking.

(e) Under conditions of phase-locking the effects of ENSO and the monsoonal system cancel each other out.

Question 3.7

Which of the following actions, if any, would be likely to contribute to the resilience of an agricultural society?

(a) Relying on market forces to distribute resources to the most needy.

(b) Stockpiling foodstuffs during years of surplus.

(c) Maximizing use of land to provide an exportable surplus.

(d) Developing and maintaining irrigation systems that store water and regulate its flow.

(e) Tax increases during periods of adversity to pay for food imports.

(f) Tax relief or concessions during periods of adversity.

Question 3.8

In three to four short sentences, describe the likely effects of a phase-locking of a downturn in the global market with a period of extreme rain deficit on a late-19th-century Indian farmer.

Question 3.9

Which of the following, if any, are examples of top-down governance?

(a) Village-level management of common lands and irrigation systems.

(b) Government taxes on all cultivated land.

(c) Redistribution of foodstuffs from regions with a food surplus to regions with a food shortfall.

(d) National policies restricting food exports during periods of adversity.

(e) The decision by farmers to plant some of their land in famine-resistant crops.

(f) The decision by farmers to plant some of their land in crops for the global market.

Question 3.10

State two reasons why global markets might be viewed as operating on an uneven playing field, rather than a level one.

References

Davis, M. (2001) *Late Victorian Holocausts: El Niño Famines and the Making of the Third World.* London: Verso.

Kripalani, R. H. and Kulkarni, A. (1997) Climatic impact of El Niño/La Nina on the Indian monsoon: a new perspective. *Weather*, **52**, pp. 39–46.

Kurlansky, M. (1999) *Cod.* London: Verso.

Marten, G. (2001) *Human Ecology: Basic Concepts for Sustainable Development.* London: Earthscan.

Pauly, D. J., Christensen, V., Guenette, S., Pitcher, T. J., Sumaila, U. R., Walters, C. J., Watson R. and Zeller, D. (2002) Towards sustainability in world fisheries. *Nature*, **418**, pp. 689–695.

Sen, A. (2001) Apocalypse then, *The New York Times* [online]. Available from: http://www.nytimes.com/books/01/02/18/reviews/010218.18senlt.html [Accessed 12 August 2002].

Scheffer, M., Carpenter, S., Foley, J. A., Folke, C. and Walker, B. (2001) Catastrophic shifts in ecosystems, *Nature*, **413**, pp. 591–596.

World Resources Institute (2000) *World Resources 2000–2001 People and Ecosystems: The Fraying Web of Life.* Washington D.C.: World Resources Institute.

4 Island Antarctica

Prepared for the course team by Mark Brandon, Nigel Clark and Marion Hall

4

4.1 Introduction

There is a long history of human interaction with island ecosystems. As we have seen, the arrival of people on any previously unsettled island has always been a risky venture — because the island ecosystem and the incoming human social systems are inevitably new to each other. However, there is evidence to suggest that over time some human populations and island ecosystems have been relatively successful in adjusting to each other. We say 'relatively' because there is always a background of uncertainty in the form of natural variations — such as El Niño events — that may push the readjusted island ecosystem beyond its limits of tolerance. But social systems also have variations, such as economic downturns, and these can also test tolerance levels. As you saw in Chapter 3, when crises in the realm of social life overlap with extremes of natural variation (Section 3.4), the result can be catastrophic in every sense. And this can occur not just on the scale of small islands but right across continents.

It is a challenge to understand how human interventions transform the natural world. This raises the issue of sustainability. However, it is even more of a challenge to come to terms with the way in which variable and unstable human social systems interact with variable and unstable natural systems. For this we need to complement the theme of sustainability with our other course themes: uncertainty, governance and globalization.

For the rest of this book we are going to investigate one system in more detail. Antarctica, though vast, is really a continent-sized island surrounded by smaller islands. For our purposes it does have one key advantage that was summed up very well by Edwin Mickleburgh:

> Less than a hundred years ago Antarctica still awaited the sound of a human voice, the imprint of a human boot. Two hundred years ago and no human eye had looked upon it. Antarctica was the object only of speculation which had absorbed philosophers and geographers alike since Aristotle first postulated the existence of a southern continent.
>
> (Mickleburgh, 1987)

Antarctica gives us a modern example of the interaction between humans and a 'pure' island ecosystem with subsequent human interaction. Although remote, the teleconnections between this region and the rest of the world are important. You have already seen one example of this in the belief of the Maldivians that the possible collapse of the West Antarctic Ice-Sheet could completely destroy their islands. This collapse could occur at the end of a set of complex feedback processes that make up the web of inter-connections between Antarctica and the rest of the world. We need to understand the interactions between these feedbacks and their potential impacts in the future.

Here you will learn about the geography, ecosystem and development of Antarctica over the last 200 years. The physical environment and the ecosystem have much inherent natural uncertainty. Coping with this uncertainty has led to the development of a special system for dealing with globalization and governance issues. But like any international solution, we will see (Chapter 6) that one may not always end up with the desired result.

Returning to the quote above, you may have been surprised to read that it was the Greek philosopher Aristotle who first thought there could be a unknown continent to the south. The Greeks named the star constellation above the North Pole *arktos*, meaning 'the bear'. The opposite end of the Earth, at the South Pole, was simply named *ant-arktos*, meaning 'the opposite of the north'. Over the years this has developed into the name Antarctica.

What do you think of when we speak of Antarctica? Take a few moments to make a mental note of the things that immediately come into your mind. You most likely thought along the lines of an icy hell, a place where nature rules, a land untouched by humans, the last wilderness and so on. You may have thought of penguins, of whales, of Captain Scott and his colleagues pulling a sledge through a terrible storm, of beautiful sunsets (Figure 4.1). Aside from these obvious and stereotypical images, what is the 'truth' about Antarctica? One very famous polar explorer described Antarctica as 'more lonely than London' (Apsley Cherry-Garrard, 1922). Does this quote tie in with the things that came into your mind? As we pointed out earlier in this book, where you sit clearly influences how you see things.

So, what is Antarctica really like — its geography, its climate and its ecosystem? How much impact have humans already had? Who lives there, who owns the land and who even cares? There is a lot of information about Antarctica on the Internet. Some of this information will be along the same lines as those you have already considered — after all the Web reflects cultural influence. However, cultural influence has produced some surprising misconceptions about the region that persist despite extensive media coverage. (Later in the course you will study the effect of the media on environmental issues in more detail.) For example, it is often written that the temperatures in Antarctica can be below –80 °C, winds can be over 250 km h^{-1}, and it is a dark and frigid place. But, how true is this and how can this common view be reconciled with the concerns of the Maldivians about global warming and imminent ice-sheet collapse?

The Internet gives us the opportunity to go beyond simple fact-gathering, because we can formulate and answer our own questions using information and data that are not

Figure 4.1 Some views of Antarctica.

available with such breadth and ease from any other source. You will learn to develop this approach throughout your study of *The Environmental Web*. Thinking about Antarctica, we begin by looking at its 'discovery'. The motivation for any geographical journey is either exploration, or exploitation, and the discovery of Antarctica was no different. So, at once we can see the role played by globalization and sustainability. We should also implicitly consider the governance of the resource being exploited, when discussing sustainability.

4.2 Early 'discoveries' of Antarctica

Although Aristotle's ideas turned out to be correct, they were not confirmed for many centuries. Sixteenth-century western maps show an outline of this supposed 'land' — but there was no proof of its existence. After the outline of 'Antarctica' first appeared on a map, its presence was propagated through successive maps as described in Box 4.1.

Box 4.1 Lost Islands

Once land appears on a map, it is actually very difficult to remove it, because deletion requires proof that the land is *not* there. Unfortunately, throughout most of human history, navigation has been a very imprecise science. A sea captain discovering land would mark it on a map, but the ship could actually have been hundreds of miles away from where it was thought to be in relation to 'known' land. Navigation was not improved until Captain Cook circumnavigated the Earth in the late 18th century with a chronometer, and precise navigation only become common in the late 19th century as the price of the chronometers fell and they became commonly available.

An example of this imprecise marine navigation can be seen in Figure 4.2, where all the islands in the South Atlantic Ocean that were removed when a 'new' British Admiralty chart was drawn in 1808 are shown in red. The oceanographer Henry Stommel researched this chart and tracked down the history of each of these 'lost islands' (Stommel, 1984). For example, he found papers suggesting that the island of Grande that was 'discovered' by Antonio de la Roche in 1675, was actually an isolated headland on the coast of South America — about 2000 km away. In the Antarctic, with ice, poor weather and cloud obscuring visibility of the skies, navigation problems were greatly increased.

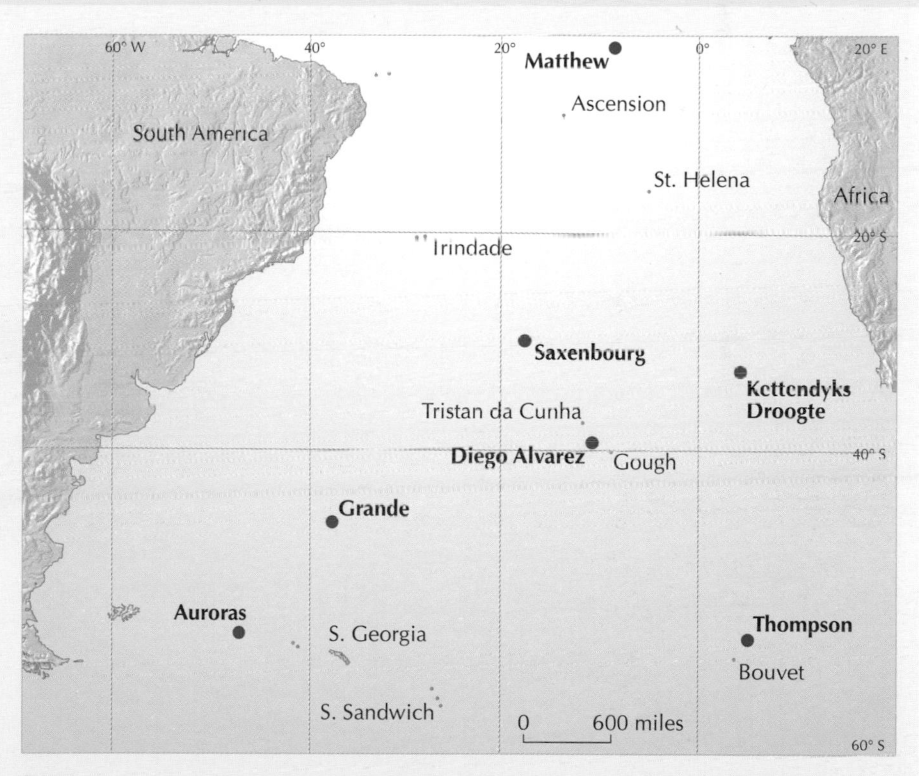

Figure 4.2 Henry Stommel's map of the islands removed from an 1808 British Admiralty map of the South Atlantic Ocean.

Soon this 'Antarctic' land was appearing on western maps with the name *Terra Australis Incognito*. As more sailors ventured south, gaps in geographical knowledge were filled. For example, in 1578 Francis Drake sailed through what became the Drake Passage and conclusively proved that any possible *Terra Australis Incognito* was not connected to South America. As usual, however, the western notion of historical discovery and exploration is not the whole story. Previously you have seen how 18th-century European sailors 'discovered' already inhabited islands. In fact, the first known Antarctic polar observations are from a Polynesian oral legend from the island of Rarotonga (Cook Islands). They tell of a chief called Ui-te-Rangiora who sailed to the Southern Ocean in a canoe around AD 650 and found ice and snow. Another Polynesian from the Cook Islands, Aru-Tanga-Nuku, is said to have repeated this amazing voyage around AD 800.

Our first 'positive' evidence for the discovery of Antarctica though, is from Captain James Cook who famously circumnavigated the globe twice before dying on his third voyage. Cook also recorded possible regions for exploitation. On his second voyage, his two ships, *Resolution* and *Adventure*, crossed the Antarctic Circle (66.5° S) in January 1773. They soon ran into an impenetrable wall of sea ice and Cook wrote in his journal that:

> The ice was so thick and close that we could proceed no further … I could see nothing to the southward but ice, in the whole extent from east to WSW without the least appearance of any partition.

(quoted in Hough, 1994)

Cook crossed the Antarctic circle on two further occasions, but despite sailing a long way south, he never found an Antarctic continent. He had, however, begun discovering the islands around Antarctica. Whilst following up various leads from another sea captain, one of Cook's officers wrote in his journal:

> We've been for these six or seven days past cruising for the land the Frenchman gave intelligence of at the Cape of Good Hope … if my friend Monsieur found any land, he's been confoundedly out in the latitude and longitude of it all, we've searched the spot he represented it being and its environs too pretty narrowly and the devil an inch of land is there …

(quoted in Hough, 1994)

Some of the islands Cook was looking for really did exist though. Although de la Roche is credited with being mistaken about Grande island, he is also credited with the first sighting of the island of South Georgia in 1675 (although this too may have been a case of mistaken identity). Cook made the first recorded landing in January 1775 and he promptly claimed it for the King with 'a descharge [sic] of small arms'. He did not like it and described it as 'savage and horrible'. However, he did think he had discovered *Terra Australis Incognito* — the problem was that it was not the resource-rich area that they had hoped for. He wrote:

> … not a tree or shrub was to be seen, no not even big enough to make a toothpick …

(quoted in Hough, 1994)

Cook began to survey the coastline and soon determined that South Georgia was only an island and he wrote:

> This land which we had taken to be part of a great continent was no more than an island of 70 leagues in circuit … Who would have thought that an island of no greater extent than this is situated between the latitude of 54° and 55° should in the very height of summer be in a manner wholly covered many fathoms deep with frozen snow …
>
> (quoted in Hough, 1994)

He left South Georgia in a south-east direction in which he discovered the South Sandwich Islands (of which you will hear more later). As *Resolution* and *Adventure* subsequently headed north, Cook was convinced that if there was an Antarctic continent it was to the south of a wall of pack ice, and if found it would also be covered in ice and snow and be a desolate place. In his private journal, he wrote that if anyone were to discover such a land 'I make bold to declare that the world will derive no benefit from it'. Although Cook did not seem to consider South Georgia to be the resource-rich area he had hoped for, he did write:

> Seals or Sea Bears were pretty numerous … the shores swarm'd with young cubs.
>
> (quoted in Hough, 1994)

So, after discovery came exploitation.

4.3 The discovery of 'real' Antarctica

Cook's naturalists were well aware that there were many other areas in the Southern Ocean that had large seal populations. But perhaps they did not understand how quickly these stocks would be over-exploited, and then crash. With the potential to obtain huge fortunes from sealing, the exploitation began in earnest. British and American sealers initially said that you could not actually land on the island of South Georgia without first killing seals, and in 1825 James Weddell calculated that 1 200 000 sealskins had been taken from South Georgia alone.

- Do you think it would have been possible to exploit the seals in a sustainable way once they were discovered?

- Our key course theme of sustainability is about exploiting a system without undermining it. Without knowledge of the natural cycles of seal populations or the uncertainty in the ecosystem, exploitation would not have been any more sustainable than the examples you have already encountered.

Weddell had a good idea of what sustainability really meant and he was saddened by this slaughter. He wrote that a sustainable harvest of skins would have allowed up to 100 000 seals being taken for many years to come, but by taking too many, the sealers had destroyed everything. The seal population first faltered and then collapsed. As South Georgia and other islands were stripped of their seal populations, the sealers had to move further and further southwards to find unexploited islands where profits would remain high. It is very difficult to piece together the exploration and exploitation activities during this period, because records of ships' movements were of course commercially valuable, and captains went to great lengths to make sure that their voyages were kept secret from competitors. What is certain is that in the next 20 years or so, Antarctica was 'discovered'. What is rather more uncertain is *who* actually discovered it.

The British view is that the English sea captain William Smith sighted land first. He was sailing in the brig *Williams* on a voyage from Buenos Aires to Valparaiso when he sighted the South Shetlands on 19 February 1819. In October of the same year Smith landed on King George Island and took possession for the King on 15 October. However, many have argued that the South Shetland Islands are not the Antarctic mainland. The Royal Navy then chartered the *Williams* with Edward Bransfield in command and on 30 January 1820 they sighted and charted Trinity Land, now the Trinity Peninsula and part of mainland Antarctica. Clearly 'delighted' at their good fortune, one of the crew wrote that the sight was 'a prospect the most gloomy that can be imagined' (Sullivan, 1957). So is Antarctica British?

Actually, the Russian Thaddeus Bellingshausen, with his ships the *Vostok* and *Mirny*, had sighted land on 15 January 1820, but he was unable to reach it. So, Bransfield appears to have been beaten by a few days, though the Russians never landed.

It would be too easy though if that was the whole story. The American view is that the sealer Nathaniel Palmer discovered Antarctica. Palmer was in command of the sloop *Hero* and at the end of January 1821 was sailing along the Antarctic Peninsula when fog descended. As the fog thinned he found himself worryingly between two large warships. Naturally he ran up his Stars and Stripes and the warships responded by hoisting the Cross of St Andrew — the flag of Imperial Russia. It was Bellingshausen again and he told Palmer that he had been beaten.

Clearly then, we have a British claim for the discovery of Antarctica, a Russian claim and finally an American claim. So, which is correct? And what about the Polynesians? Indeed by now you may even be thinking 'is this important?' It is important because Antarctica has rich resources and the discoverer of the region could legitimately lay claim to these resources — as indeed the Europeans had done previously in many other parts of the inhabited world.

So, who discovered Antarctica? The reality may well be that it was none of these three 19th-century characters. There were at least 50 sealing ships operating in the region at this time, but because of commercial priorities they kept their location secret.

Once nations cottoned on to the 'limitless' resources, over the next 100 years a series of expeditions set out to discover the extent of this region. With poor equipment and only sailing ships, the people on these expeditions suffered terrible and famous hardships, and this period in polar history has become known as the 'heroic age'. Table 4.1 lists some of the key expeditions in this period, some of which have provided us with famous and enduring images of Antarctica, such as Shackleton's trapped ship *Endurance* (Figure 4.3).

There are almost certainly some expeditions in Table 4.1 that you have heard of, but there are also many that you may not be familiar with, such as that of William Bruce (1902) with the ship *Scotia*. His Scottish National Antarctic Expedition was scientifically a great success. In the same way that the modern day media trumpets 'bad' news, the

Figure 4.3 Shackleton's ship *Endurance* trapped in the sea ice of the Weddell Sea.

same was true of the last century and so, like other successful expeditions to the Antarctic, this one is not well known.

Table 4.1 Some of the key expeditions to Antarctica.

Year	Expedition
1773	Captain James Cook (British) crosses the Antarctic Circle
1820	Thaddeus Thaddevich Bellingshausen (Russian) makes the first sighting of the Antarctic continent
1820	Edward Bransfield (British) makes the first sighting of the Antarctic Peninsula
1821	Nathanial Palmer (American) sights Palmers Land
1840	Jules Sebastian Dumont d'Urville (French) discovers Terre Adélie
1873	Edward Dallman leads the first German Antarctic Expedition
1897	De Gerlache leads the Belgian Antarctic Expedition on the ship *Belgica*
1901	Nordenskjöld leads the Swedish South Polar Expedition on the ship *Antarctic*
1901	Scott leads the British National Antarctic Expedition on the ship *Discovery* and makes the first extensive inland journeys
1902	William Bruce leads the Scottish National Antarctic Expedition to the South Orkney Islands on the ship *Scotia*
1903	Jean Charcot leads the French Antarctic Expedition on the ship *Français*
1907	Shackleton leads the British Antarctic Expedition on the ship *Nimrod* and gets to within 108 miles of the South Pole
1910	Scott leads the British Antarctic Expedition on the ship *Terra Nova*. He reaches the South Pole on 18 January 1912 but he and his four companions die on the return journey
1910	Amundsen leads the Norwegian Antarctic Expedition on the ship *Fram* and reaches the South Pole on 14 December 1911
1910	Shirase leads the Japanese Antarctic Expedition on the *Kainan Maru*
1911	Filchner leads the German South Polar Expedition on the *Deutschland*
1911	Douglas Mawson leads the Australasian Antarctic Expedition on the ship *Aurora*
1914	Shackleton leads the Imperial Trans-Antarctic Expedition on the ship *Endurance*. His ship is crushed on the pack ice before reaching the continent but he manages to lead his men to safety after drifting with the sea-ice for over a year

Whilst all of the heroic expeditions listed in the table were in progress, there were also numerous sealer and whaler voyages to the Antarctic during this period. Most were secret but some were not.

- What do you notice about the nationalities of the people listed in Table 4.1?
- The majority are from the colonial powers of the 19th century.

Most of the sealers and whalers also belonged to the countries listed in Table 4.1. For example, when Scott was trapped in Antarctica in 1901, the Dundee whaling ship *Morning* was sent to rescue him. In the same way that the rest of the world was being exploited by the colonial powers in the 19th century, so too was Antarctica being exploited by these *same* colonial powers. The pressures of globalization meant that the distribution of resources in Antarctica was, as usual, not equitable. Now we have briefly described the discovery of Antarctica, we will turn to what these explorers and exploiters actually discovered.

4.4 Antarctic geography

4.4.1 Maps of Antarctica

The best starting point for an investigation into Antarctic geography is to examine an up-to-date map of Antarctica. You may think that 'up to date' is rather a strange phrase to use when talking about maps and geography, but you will find out that our uncertainty about Antarctica extends not only to the ecosystem, but also to the shape of Antarctica itself.

Figure 4.4 shows a map of Antarctica downloaded from the Internet in 2002. You should be able to find others on the Internet that are similar and hopefully more recent. This type of map is called a **polar projection** and is unfamiliar to most people. Imagine looking at the Earth from a point in space directly over the South Pole. The continent would be stretched over the shape of the Earth with the South Pole at the centre. Then, if the outline of the continent were to be lifted from the Earth and flattened onto a piece of paper, the result would be the outline shown in Figure 4.4. Many maps (e.g. an Ordnance Survey map of the UK) are **Mercator projections** in which lines of latitude (distance from the Equator) run along the horizontal axis, and lines of longitude (the distance from the 'Prime Meridian' at 0° that runs north–south though Greenwich, UK) run along the vertical axis. In a polar projection, lines of equal latitude are shown as concentric circles expanding from the centre of the map. The largest complete circle in Figure 4.4 is the latitude line of 50° S.

- As the circles get smaller, how do the latitude and the distance from the Equator change?
- Both the latitude and the distance from the Equator increase.

At the centre of the map, the South Pole is at 90° S and the latitude 'circle' is of course a dot. Lines of longitude on a polar projection are shown as radii that expand from the centre. At the top of the map is the 0° meridian, and then moving clockwise around the map, at 3 o'clock is 90° E, at 6 o'clock is 180° E (or 180° W) and at 9 o'clock is 90° W.

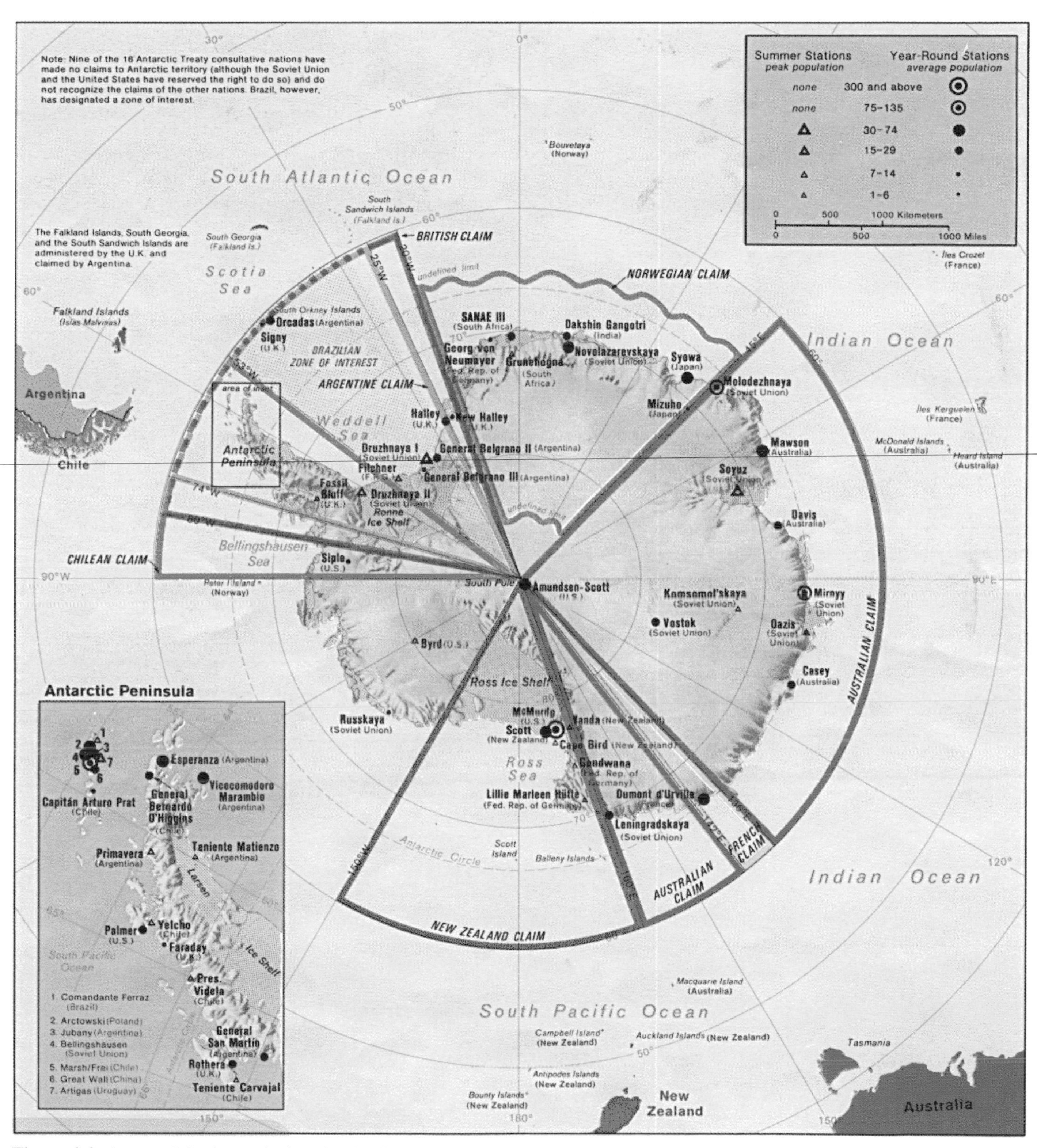

Figure 4.4 A map of the Antarctic downloaded from the Internet (CARA, 2002).

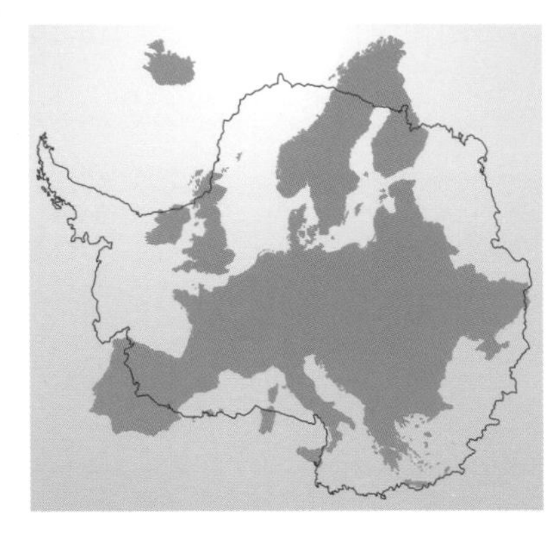

Figure 4.5 The outline of Antarctica overlaid on a shaded map of Europe drawn to the same scale.

- Maps often have an arrow on them pointing north. Why doesn't the map in Figure 4.4?
- There isn't a single direction that is 'north' on this map because in whichever direction you move from the South Pole, you go north. Therefore, it is impossible to represent the direction of north with a single arrow.

There are numerous other ways of 'projecting' maps, apart from a Mercator projection or a polar projection. One feature you can see in Figure 4.4 is that Antarctica is roughly circular in shape. The only major exception to this is at approximately 60° W (about 10 o'clock) where a finger of land extends northwards. This finger of land is called the Antarctic Peninsula, and in Chapter 6 you will see that it has a special place in Antarctic governance.

- Do you recognize any of the names of the places in Figure 4.4?
- There are some regions and places named after the people in Table 4.1.

If you are not very familiar with a polar plot it may be difficult to estimate how large the Antarctic actually is when compared with other, more familiar, continents. Figure 4.5 shows the outline of Antarctica overlaid on an outline of Europe drawn to the same scale, and it reveals that Antarctica is really quite large — at least as big as Europe.

Can a map of Antarctica tell us anything about the current governance? If we look in detail at this continent, Figure 4.4 has many coloured radii extending from the South Pole that divide the continent up into pie-shaped segments. Each of the segments bounded by a different colour is labelled as a 'claim'.

- Are all of the segments bounded by a different colour discrete, or do some of them overlap?
- Some segments overlap at the Antarctic Peninsula.

What this might mean will be discussed below, but for now let us investigate a simpler region bounded by only one pair of coloured radii. From 45° E to 136° E there is an area bounded by green lines and labelled 'Australian Claim'. This area contains land that is claimed by the Australian Government as Australian territory, and in Figure 4.4 there are several places within this region marked with a black dot or triangle. On a map of another part of the world, such dots might represent towns or cities, but here they are research stations. If you concentrate specifically on the region claimed by Australia, you can see that some of the black dots and triangles, such as Casey, have 'Australia' next to them in brackets. However, you can also see Vostok and several other stations with 'Soviet Union' in brackets within this 'Australian Claim'.

- What do you think the relevance of the country name is?
- The country given in brackets is the country that operates the research station.

Consequently, within the Australian Antarctic Territory there are research stations that have been built and are operated by the Soviet Union. Doesn't this seem strange? If the Australian Antarctic Territory has the same legal status as other Australian Territory, it is the equivalent of the Soviet Union building a research base in, for example, Tasmania. Antarctica must have some special legal status that allows countries to build scientific bases within regions 'claimed' by others.

- Why is it odd that, according to this map, the Soviet Union has bases in the Antarctic?

- The Soviet Union has not existed as such since its break up into individual states in 1990.

Clearly this is yet another example of why you have to be careful of material on the Web.

- Looking closely at the Australian segment, what else do you notice about the way the research stations are located?

- Nearly all of the stations are on the edge of the Antarctic continent. There are very few stations away from the coast.

In fact, when we look at the entire map, almost all of the stations are on the coast. Could this be telling us something about the geography and climate of Antarctica and the nature of scientific research there?

If you look again at Figure 4.4, and the regions claimed by different countries, what else strikes you as unusual when you look at which countries have actually made territorial claims? Australia, New Zealand, Chile and Argentina are relatively close to Antarctica and claims by them are not surprising. But why should countries such as France, Norway and Britain claim parts of Antarctica when they are so far away? In contrast, others such as the Soviet Union (now Russia and the Ukraine), the USA, South Africa, India, Japan and Germany have apparently not claimed territory in Antarctica. In Chapter 6, we will see that countries operating research stations on Antarctica are not all shown in Figure 4.4. There are many others, such as Korea, China, Sweden, Italy and Poland that have also not made territorial claims. What can all this mean?

The simple map from the Internet in Figure 4.4 has clearly opened up some very interesting questions about the governance of Antarctica and its globalization, as well as the operation of scientific research there.

> You should now go to the Web and do the activities associated with this part of Chapter 4.

4.4.2 Facts about Antarctica

Figure 4.4 shows that there is clearly something unusual about the governance of Antarctica. To learn more let us approach the problem in a different way. There are many resources on the Web that give useful information about the countries of the world. While we were writing this chapter, one of the simplest available was the World Flag Database (2002) website, which listed some very basic 'facts' about each country. According to this site, in 2002 Antarctica apparently had: the status of a 'Non-UN Country'; an area of 15 500 000 km^2; a capital city at the Amundsen–Scott Base at the South Pole; and its spoken languages were English, French, Norwegian and Spanish.

- Is this last 'fact' concerning language likely to be true?

- No. If it were, it would mean that all the other nationals working in Antarctica, such as the Chinese, Indian and Polish scientists, do not speak their own language in the research stations run by their respective countries. Clearly this is *not* a reliable source and Chinese dialects, Hindi and Polish for example are quite obviously spoken in this international territory.

Clearly, the World Flag Database is not a reliable source of information. We could investigate what is meant by 'Non-UN Country', for example by visiting the United Nations website to find out exactly what a 'UN country' is. Instead we will use another source that has a reputation for being more reliable than this simple World Flag Database. The United States Central Intelligence Agency, more commonly known as the CIA, publishes a book called the *CIA World Factbook* as an easily available central reference of data on each country in the world. Designed for government use, it is well researched and, although not presented in a very exciting way, is reasonably reliable and updated annually. It is also available online (the *CIA World Factbook*, 2001). However, the information is presented in a standard format so there is little guidance about what these facts mean, or how to interpret them. In the site we have chosen to illustrate our points here (2001), there were the same nine headings for every country, and consequently, you should not expect all of the headings to contain very useful information for Antarctica.

Box 4.2 shows some of the *CIA World Factbook* information available for Antarctica in 2001. You already know (Figure 4.4) that a number of countries have set up year-round research stations. But perhaps you did not know that the first balloon flight in Antarctica was made by the British explorer Robert Falcon Scott. However, there is some further information that could help to explain why, for example, Russia has a base in Australian Antarctic Territory.

- What information is this?
- The part that says 'Seven [countries] have made territorial claims, but no other country recognizes these claims. In order to form a legal framework for the activities of nations on the continent, an Antarctic Treaty was negotiated that neither denies nor gives recognition to existing territorial claims; signed in 1959, it entered into force in 1961'.

Russia does not recognize the Australian Antarctic Territory. You can now see that the Internet allows you to answer easy questions very quickly. For example, you can find a map to answer the question 'what shape is Antarctica?' and you can discover that apparently nobody owns Antarctica. But it clearly does not help with very difficult questions such as 'why would a country go to the trouble of claiming part of Antarctica if no other country will recognize the claim?' We will address the way that this system of governance has evolved in Chapter 6.

Box 4.2 Some details about Antarctica from the *CIA World Factbook* (2001)

Background

Speculation over the existence of a 'southern land' was not confirmed until the early 1820s when British and American commercial operators and British and Russian national expeditions began exploring the Peninsula region and areas south of the Antarctic Circle. Not until 1838 was it established that Antarctica was indeed a continent and not just a group of islands. Various 'firsts' were achieved in the early 20th century, including: 1902, first balloon flight (by British explorer Robert Falcon Scott); 1912, first to the South Pole (five Norwegian explorers under Roald Amundsen); 1928, first fixed-wing aircraft flight (by Australian adventurer/explorer Sir Hubert Wilkins); 1929, first flight over the South Pole (by Americans Richard Byrd and Bernt Balchen); and 1935, first transantarctic flight (American Lincoln Ellsworth). Following World War II, there was an upsurge in scientific research on the continent. A number of countries have set up year-round research stations on Antarctica. Seven have made territorial claims, but no other country recognizes these claims. In order to form a legal framework for the activities of nations on the continent, an Antarctic Treaty was negotiated that neither denies nor gives recognition to existing territorial claims; signed in 1959, it entered into force in 1961.

Geography

Location: continent mostly south of the Antarctic Circle

Geographic coordinates:
90 00 S, 0 00 E

Map references:
Antarctic Region

Area: total: 14 million km^2
land: 14 million km^2

(280 000 km^2 ice-free,
13.72 million km^2 ice-covered) (est.)

note: fifth-largest continent, following Asia, Africa, North America, and South America, but larger than Australia and the subcontinent of Europe

Area — comparative: slightly less than 1.5 times the size of the US

Land boundaries: 0 km
note: see entry on International disputes.

Coastline: 17 968 km^2

Maritime claims: none; 19 out of 26 Antarctic consultative nations have made no claims to Antarctic territory (although Russia and the US have reserved the right to do so) and do not recognize the claims of the other nations; see also the Disputes — international entry.

Climate: severe low temperatures vary with latitude, elevation, and distance from the ocean; East Antarctica is colder than West Antarctica because of its higher elevation; Antarctic Peninsula has the most moderate climate; higher temperatures occur in January along the coast and average slightly below freezing.

Terrain: about 98% thick continental ice-sheet and 2% barren rock, with average elevations between 2000 and 4000 meters; mountain ranges up to 5140 meters; ice-free coastal areas include parts of southern Victoria Land, Wilkes Land, the Antarctic Peninsula area, and parts of Ross Island on McMurdo Sound; glaciers form ice-shelves along about half of the coastline, and floating ice-shelves constitute 11% of the area of the continent.

Elevation extremes: lowest point: Bentley Subglacial Trench—2540 m
highest point: Vinson Massif 5140 m

note: the lowest known land point in Antarctica is hidden in the Bentley Subglacial Trench; at its surface is the deepest ice yet discovered and the world's lowest elevation not under sea water.

Natural resources: iron ore, chromium, copper, gold, nickel, platinum and other minerals, and coal and hydrocarbons have been found in small uncommercial quantities; none presently exploited; krill, finfish, and crab have been taken by commercial fisheries.

Land use:

arable land:	0%
permanent crops:	0%
permanent pastures:	0%
forests and woodland:	0%
other: 100% (ice 98%, barren rock	2%)

Irrigated land: 0 sq km (1993)

Natural hazards: katabatic (gravity-driven) winds blow coastward from the high interior; frequent blizzards form near the foot of the plateau; cyclonic storms form over the ocean and move clockwise along the coast; volcanism on Deception Island and isolated areas of West Antarctica; other seismic activity rare and weak; large icebergs may calve from ice-shelf.

Environment — current issues: in 1998, NASA satellite data showed that the antarctic ozone hole was the largest on record, covering 27 million square kilometers; in 1997, researchers found that increased ultraviolet light coming through the hole damages the DNA of icefish, an antarctic fish lacking hemoglobin; ozone depletion earlier was shown to harm one-celled antarctic marine plants.

Geography — note: the coldest, windiest, highest (on average), and driest continent; during summer, more solar radiation reaches the surface at the South Pole than is received at the Equator in an equivalent period; mostly uninhabitable.

Before moving on, look at the *Geography* section for Antarctica in Box 4.2. The fourth entry gives the area of Antarctica as 14 million km^2, of which 280 000 km^2 is ice free with the remaining 13.72 million km^2 covered in ice. There is also a note saying that Antarctica is the fifth largest continent on Earth. This all sounds like very useful information. However, look back to the information about Antarctica from the World Flags Database.

- What figure did it give for the area of Antarctica?
- The area of Antarctica is given as 15 500 000 km^2.

- How does this compare with the area given by the *CIA World Factbook*?
- There is a difference of 1 500 000 km^2.

This difference in area is over six times the total area of the UK. So which source should you believe? We think that the *CIA World Factbook* entry is more reliable, though we do not know where their information came from either. Clearly finding out 'facts' about Antarctica is going to be much harder than you perhaps imagined. With such an obvious discrepancy, can the other entries in the Geography section of the *CIA World Factbook* be trusted? You are probably safe in assuming that Antarctica really is the fifth largest continent, but how useful is that? The Climate entry consists of some rather general statements, while the Terrain and Elevation extremes entries are a bit more detailed, listing for example ice-free areas of coast and giving figures for average elevation, the highest mountains, the lowest point, and the percentage of bare rock. There are also many interesting facts; for example, Antarctica has the lowest elevation on the Earth that is not under seawater — the Bentley Subglacial Trench which is an extraordinary 2540 m below sea-level (*CIA World Factbook, 2001* site). The Natural resources entry lists several resources, but in quantities said to be 'uncommercial', with none being presently exploited. It also says that there has been commercial fishing. The Land use entry puts the continent entirely in a category called 'other'.

- What does 'other' mean in this context?
- The land consists entirely of something other than arable land, permanent crops, permanent pasture, or forests and woodlands.

It is not surprising then to see in the next entry that there is no irrigated land in Antarctica. There follows a list of various natural hazards such as blizzards, volcanoes and icebergs, and then a piece describing the Antarctic ozone hole as the most important current environmental issue in the region. The last note says that Antarctica is the 'coldest', 'windiest', 'highest', and 'driest continent', and that:

> ... during summer, more solar radiation reaches the surface at the South Pole than is received at the Equator in an equivalent period ...

It is difficult to interpret what the authors of the *World Factbook* mean by this last statement, but it certainly sounds surprising and we will return to this later. Finally, we note that Antarctica is 'mostly uninhabitable'.

By going to the Internet we have found 'facts', but what do they mean? The real issue is what have we learned about Antarctica from this 'reputable' source? Has it changed any of the perceptions that you may have and which were possibly illustrated in

Figure 4.1? We have a serious doubt about the accuracy of at least one of the facts, about the area of Antarctica. So, can we rely on the other facts? There are many statements that are practically impossible to contradict. But again we return to the real question. Have we learned anything about Antarctica from this source? Broadly speaking, if we know where to look, it would appear we can use the Internet to answer relatively easy questions such as 'how high is the highest mountain in Antarctica?', but it is much harder to answer complex questions such as 'why do two Internet sites give different information on something as straightforward as the area of Antarctica?'

- Can you think of two reasons why the figures given for the area of Antarctica are different?

- Both figures could be wrong — we cannot tell without seeing the sources of the data. It could also be that both numbers were correct *when they were published*, e.g. the larger number could have been the area of Antarctica before a large ice-shelf broke off and reduced the area to the smaller number.

Figure 4.6 A satellite photograph showing the collapse of part of the Larsen-B Ice-Shelf in 2002.

The second reason is plausible. Although a difference of six times the area of the UK sounds a lot, large chunks of ice-shelf break off from Antarctica relatively frequently. For example, in the year 2000, a giant iceberg measuring 6800 km^2 broke off from an ice-shelf and started drifting northwards away from Antarctica, and in 2002 about 3200 km^2 of the Larsen-B Ice-Shelf on the eastern side of the Antarctic Peninsula spectacularly shattered (Figure 4.6) in only 35 days.

Statements on an Internet site have the same problems as any unreferenced source. It is not possible to know if they are true, false, or were true at a particular time. An added problem of the Web is the ease of access to information. The temptation is to use the first source found, without justification. We hope that this simple example of a relatively straightforward 'fact' about Antarctica (the land area) has demonstrated the seriousness of this potential problem.

So far we have found out quite a lot about Antarctica. However, if you want to use the Internet in a different and more advanced way, then you need to do some planning first, and in the next section we introduce a scheme to help focus your efforts.

4.5 A short interlude — using the Internet for research

Answers to straightforward questions such as the shape of Antarctica are quick and simple. However, one of the wonders of the Internet is that it is actually possible to go much further than this. We can access *raw* data, carry out our own analysis, and draw appropriate conclusions. Although this is going much further than many people who use the Internet, later in the course you will see that this method of working is very similar to the way that for example a journalist or scientist would conduct research. To be really efficient of course, you should never sit down at a computer until you know what you 'don't know'. Or to put it another way, first you need to define a question. Questions such as 'Why is there a Rusian base in Australian Antarctic Territory?' require more forethought than straightforward ones. To help you with these more difficult questions we have devised a series of steps that you can follow (Figure 4.7, overleaf).

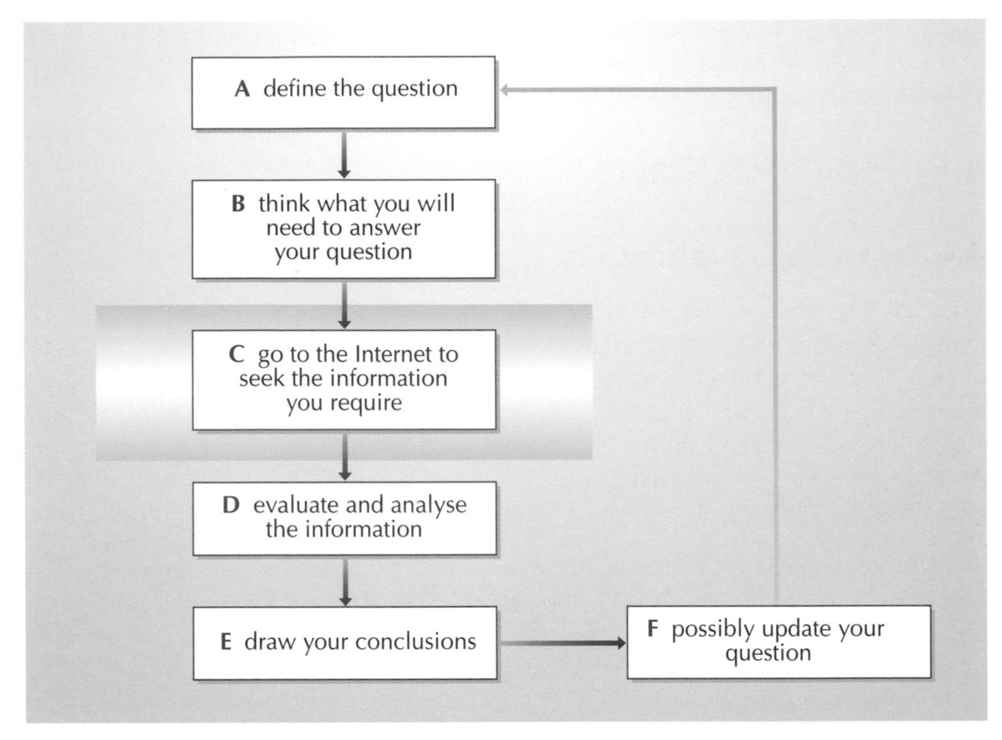

Figure 4.7 A schematic outline of a process for using the Internet to answer a question.

Once you have chosen a question to ask, you should think carefully about the sort of information you would need to answer it. For example, imagine you are an engineer and have been asked to build a bridge across a river.

- What sort of information would you need before building the bridge?
- You would need to know: how wide the river is, what load the bridge is to take, the depth of the river, and so on.

An engineer starts with the specification for the job. However, as you have come to appreciate, the difficult nature of environmental questions requires a strict specification. If your aim is to convince someone in another part of the world that they should change their lifestyle to help you, you need to be precise about what they will gain as a result. So, in the schematic in Figure 4.7, Box A is relatively easy. The real problem is always going to be Box B: specifying what you need. Once you have this, Box C, the step that is online, is going to be focused and relatively short.

When you have found your information you must evaluate it, and then finally in Box E, draw your conclusions. Once you have answered even a simple question, you can follow the arrow to Box F and update your question to further your understanding. The key point is to use the Internet in short focused bursts rather than becoming sidetracked (step C). The more specific you are about the sort of information you intend to recover, and how you are then going to analyse it, the more successful your search will be. It means overall that you can be much more effective during your time spent online. You may find it helpful to refer back to Figure 4.7 until you have learned this, or found a similarly effective way of working online.

The geography part of the *World Factbook* entry (see Box 4.2) stated that there are 'severe low temperatures' in Antarctica. In the next section, you will follow the schematic shown in Figure 4.7 to find out what the climate of Antarctica is actually like in this 'cold and frigid' place.

4.6 Antarctic climate

4.6.1 Air temperatures

What do you think of when you imagine the air temperatures of Antarctica? Low temperatures definitely, but how cold? Our perceptions are clouded by previous exposure to relevant information. In the case of Antarctica, many British people imagine Captain Scott dying on his return from the South Pole with his party suffering terribly (Figure 4.8). You may have seen wildlife programmes on television about the Emperor penguin, *Aptenodytes forsteri*, a bird that hatches and brings up its chicks in the deep Antarctic midwinter (Figure 4.9). If so, you may agree with the polar explorer Apsley Cherry-Garrard, who said:

> Take it all in all, I do not believe anybody on Earth has a worse time than an Emperor penguin.
>
> (Apsley Cherry-Garrard, 1922)

Figure 4.9 An Emperor penguin rearing its chick in the Antarctic winter.

Both images certainly suggest that conditions would be horrendous for us. But is it actually like that the whole year round? For example, if we were to look at mean air temperatures taken over a whole month for the UK, the 'normal' seasonal range would be from perhaps 3 °C to 18 °C. Would you expect a similar range of air temperatures in Antarctica? You may not even have imagined Antarctica as having different seasons, that is a winter, spring, summer and autumn. By following the scheme in Figure 4.7 you can use the Internet to answer questions about Antarctic temperatures.

Figure 4.8 Scott's party sledging in a blizzard, sketched by Edward Wilson, one of the party who died with Scott.

Now go to the Web and do the activities associated with this part of Chapter 4.

4.6.2 Mean temperatures across Antarctica

Figure 4.10 shows the mean temperatures for the southern summer and winter in Antarctica. The circular lines labelled –30, –20, 0 and so on, are in degrees Celsius and represent lines of equal temperature. These are called **isotherms**. If you look at the South Pole in Figure 4.10a, it lies between the –20 °C and the –30 °C isotherm. This means that the mean summer temperature at this location is between these two temperatures.

- Assuming that the change in temperature between these two isotherms is linear — that is, it varies in proportion to the distance from them, estimate the temperature at the South Pole.

- The South Pole is closer to the –30 °C isotherm, so the mean summer temperature is probably about –28 °C.

The 0 °C degree temperature line circumscribes Antarctica in Figure 4.10a, and in some regions such as the Antarctic Peninsula, it is very close to the land. In other regions, such as the Weddell Sea and Ross Sea (see Figure 4.4), the 0 °C isotherm is a long way from land.

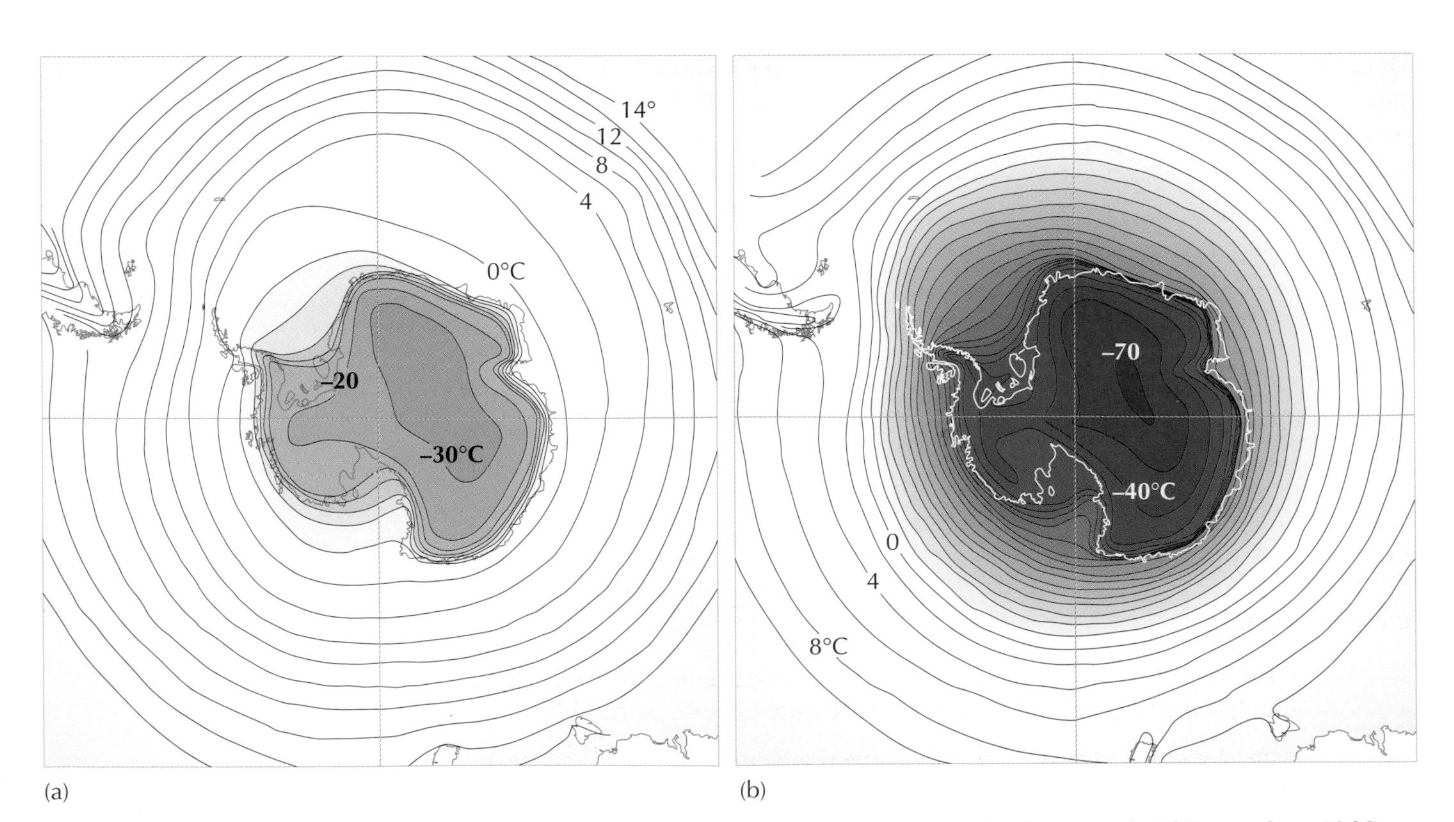

Figure 4.10 The mean surface temperatures for the southern hemisphere. (a) Summer. The isotherms are in 2 °C steps from 12 °C to –10 °C, and then in steps of 10 °C. (b) Winter. The isotherms are in 2 °C steps from 10 °C to 0 °C, in 1 °C steps from 0 °C to –10 °C, and 5 °C steps from –10 °C to –70 °C.

- Assume again that the temperature change between isotherms is linear. When isotherms are close together, is the temperature change with distance rapid or slow?

- It is rapid.

Where isotherms are widely spaced, the opposite is true and there is little variation in temperature over long distances. Looking at Figure 4.10a again, in the middle of the Weddell Sea you could move a few hundred kilometres towards the South Pole and the mean summer temperature would only change by about 2–3 °C. In contrast, at a longitude of 90 °W, if you moved from the coast towards the South Pole by a similar distance, the temperature change could be as much as 20 °C. However, the mean summer temperature of most of the coast of Antarctica is about −2 °C.

The corresponding picture for the mean winter temperatures is very different (Figure 4.10b). The distance between isotherms is fairly constant from the −70 °C isotherm all the way out to the 0 °C isotherm (taking the varying steps between isotherms into account).

- What is the mean winter temperature at the coast of Antarctica?

- About −10 to −15 °C.

From the coast out to the 0 °C isotherm, the change in mean surface winter temperature seems to be related to the distance from the coast. You can see that the Antarctic Peninsula does have some effect on the shape of these isotherms, as do the very large Filchner–Ronne and Ross Ice-Shelves (see Figure 4.4 for the location of these areas; the Filchner Ice-Shelf is continuous with and east of the Ronne Ice-Shelf). Figure 4.10 shows clearly that the regions close to the sea have temperatures in quite a narrow range. In summer most of the Antarctic Peninsula is above 0 °C. Winter is more harsh at the coasts, but still no worse than some regions of the planet that are inhabited. In contrast, central Antarctica is very different.

You may be thinking by now that, as the 0 °C isotherm is out over the ocean, does this mean that the ocean freezes? The answer is yes, and this will be discussed in Chapter 5. Before that, however, there is one more important feature of the Antarctic climate to be considered and this is the seasonal cycle.

4.6.3 The seasonal cycle of atmospheric temperature in Antarctica

Figure 4.11 (overleaf) shows the seasonal temperature cycle at Adelaide Island, now called Rothera Point (a research station operated by the British Antarctic Survey on the northwest coast of the Antarctic Peninsula) over a 2-year period from December 1964 to December 1966. These dates were chosen because they are in the middle of the temperature record.

- Is the pattern (though not necessarily the actual temperatures) of the record for Adelaide Island in Figure 4.11 the same as you might expect in the UK?

- No, in the Southern Hemisphere the summer solstice is in December instead of June.

Thus there are warmer summer temperatures from December through to April, then a gradual fall during autumn down to minimum winter temperatures in June and July.

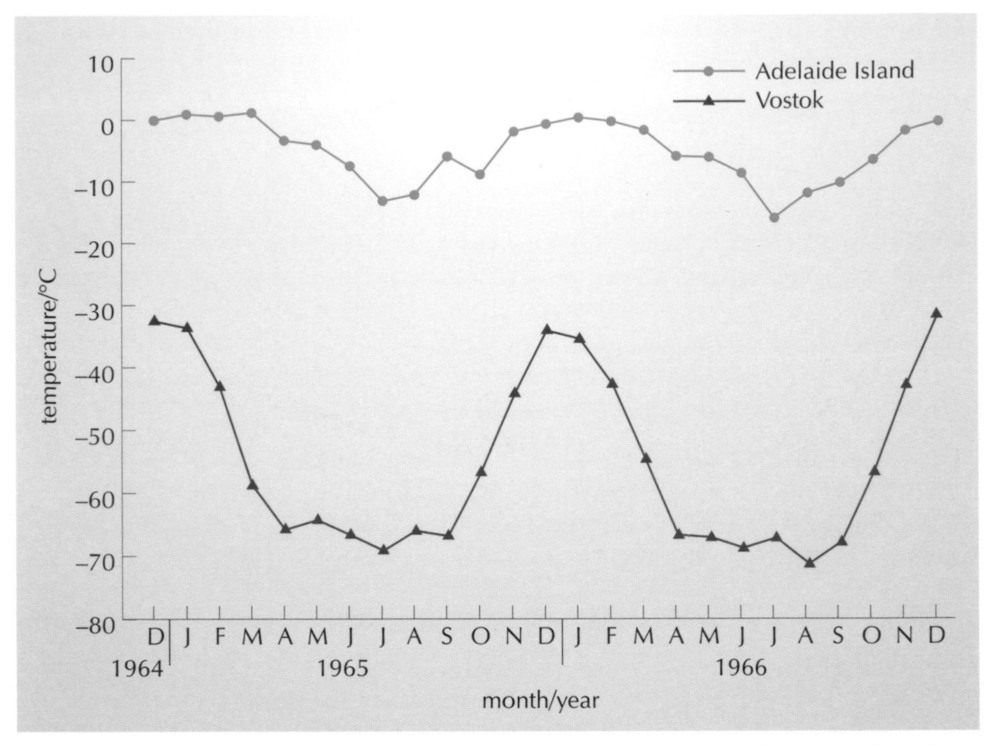

Figure 4.11 Seasonal atmospheric temperature cycle at the research stations Adelaide Island and Vostok.

In spring, temperatures rise slowly again to reach a maximum in the summer months. Broadly speaking, the record shows the same pattern in both years, with differences attributable to slightly different conditions in each year; for example in 1966 there was a colder winter.

Figure 4.11 also shows the seasonal cycle at Vostok over the same period. Remember that Vostok is a research station operated by Russia deep inland on the Antarctic Plateau (see Figure 4.4). It has the distinction of being the place where the coldest temperature on Earth has been recorded (−89.2 °C). The question of why anyone would want to put a research station in such a savagely cold and remote place is addressed in Chapter 6. Comparing the seasonal cycle at Vostok with that at Adelaide Island shows striking differences.

- What are the two main differences?
- In Vostok, summer is comparatively short, with a rapid rise in temperature followed by a rapid fall and winter is long and cold with temperatures approximately constant, showing no distinct minimum.

The absence of a distinct minimum winter temperature on the Antarctic Plateau has led to the winter being called a **coreless winter**. This is one of the major differences between the Antarctic continent away from the oceans, and the rest of the planet.

Surface temperatures are mainly determined by the amount of energy from the Sun (incident solar radiation) that actually reaches the Earth. The further away from the Equator we go, the less energy reaches the Earth's surface, and so temperatures are generally lower. You may already know that the Earth is actually inclined at approximately 23.5° to the Sun (Figure 4.12). What this means in practice is that in the Antarctic winter, there is no incident solar radiation reaching the Earth south of 66.5° S

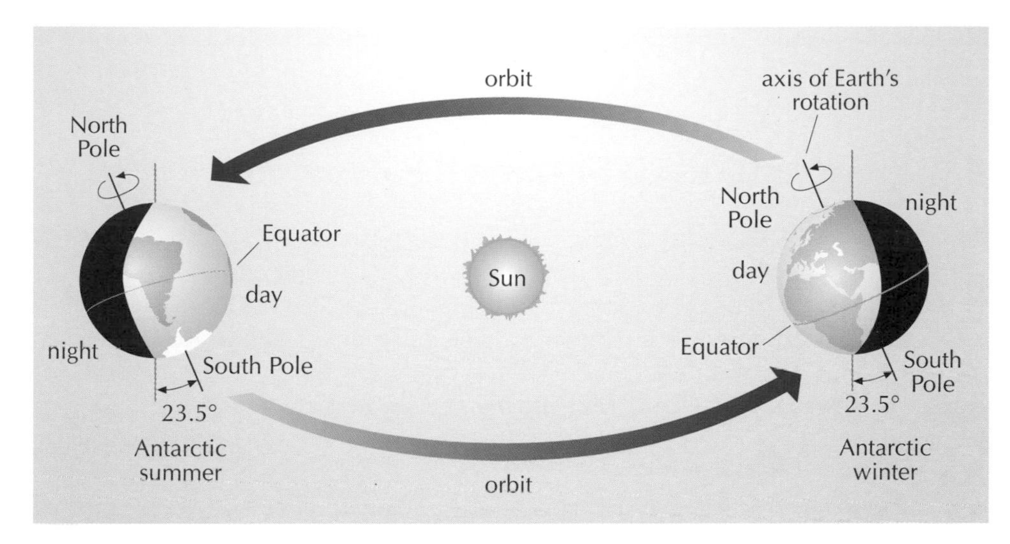

Figure 4.12 The orbit of the Earth showing why the Antarctic is completely dark for part of the year.

at any time of day. North of 66.5° S there is only a very short day that increases in length the further north you go. At the tip of the Antarctic Peninsula during the winter solstice, there are only a few hours when the Sun is above the horizon. South of 66.5° S, as winter approaches and the Sun starts to disappear for longer and longer each day, the atmosphere loses heat because there is less and less incident solar radiation to keep it warm. The ocean provides another source of heat that also affects atmospheric temperatures. In the same way that the water in a car radiator moves heat away from the engine, the ocean moves heat around the planet. During the Antarctic winter, the sea is relatively warm compared with the atmosphere and so acts as a source of heat for the coastal regions. However, inland the heat loss is so great that the temperature falls rapidly to effectively the lowest temperature it can reach. With no further cooling possible, and no source of heating either from the Sun or from the ocean, the temperature stays approximately constant, producing the coreless winter.

In the Antarctic summer south of 66.5° S, Antarctica is continually illuminated by the Sun. Incident solar radiation is therefore at a maximum and temperatures rapidly rise as shown in Figure 4.11.

The *CIA World Factbook* states that 'during summer, more solar radiation reaches the surface at the South Pole than is received at the Equator in an equivalent period'. You can see from Figure 4.12 why this is the case. At the Equator the Earth receives about 12 hours of sunlight per day constantly throughout the year. This can be compared with the 24 hours of sunlight the South Pole receives in summer. But as most of this energy is instantly reflected out to space by the snow and ice it does not increase temperatures very much, and so the central Antarctic is still a pretty hostile place.

Understanding how the Earth orbits around the Sun, and which parts are in daylight and night-time in different seasons can be rather difficult to understand. Probably for the same reason, clockmakers in the 17th and 18th centuries built mechanical models to show the orbits of the planets around the Sun. Such an **orrery** (Figure 4.13) is a beautiful piece of engineering and watching one work is a wonderful thing. The name orrery comes from the second model ever made, which was for the Earl of Orrery. Most of us are not rich enough to afford such a beautiful instrument but by searching for 'orrery' it is possible to find digital alternatives on the Internet, thus illustrating the

Figure 4.13 The solar system model, or orrery, made by John Rowley of London for Charles Boyle, fourth Earl of Orrery, in 1712. The model shows the motions of the Earth and Moon around the Sun.

fact that the Internet is not merely a source of information, but it can also help you understand that information.

4.7 How Antarctica became ice covered

We finish this chapter by explaining how Antarctica became ice covered. You may know that the shape of the continents have not been constant throughout the 4.5 billion-year history of the Earth. The continents sit on plates that drift and move around the planet over time. If we go back in time and trace this continental drift, Antarctica was at 30° S (Figure 4.14a) only about 195 million years ago (195 Ma), and so mostly ice free at that time. As the continent drifted southwards (Figure 4.14b), average temperatures decreased and precipitation began to turn to snow and settle on the land. This probably happened in the last 20 million years although we cannot be certain to within about 5 million years. Once snow began to settle, it reflected a greater amount of incident solar radiation out to space.

- What would have been the effect of reflecting more solar radiation out to space, rather than absorbing it?
- The heat from the solar radiation would have been lost and the continent would have cooled even more rapidly.

Even with a maximum incident solar radiation, the energy reaching the surface at high latitudes was far too low to raise air temperatures significantly.

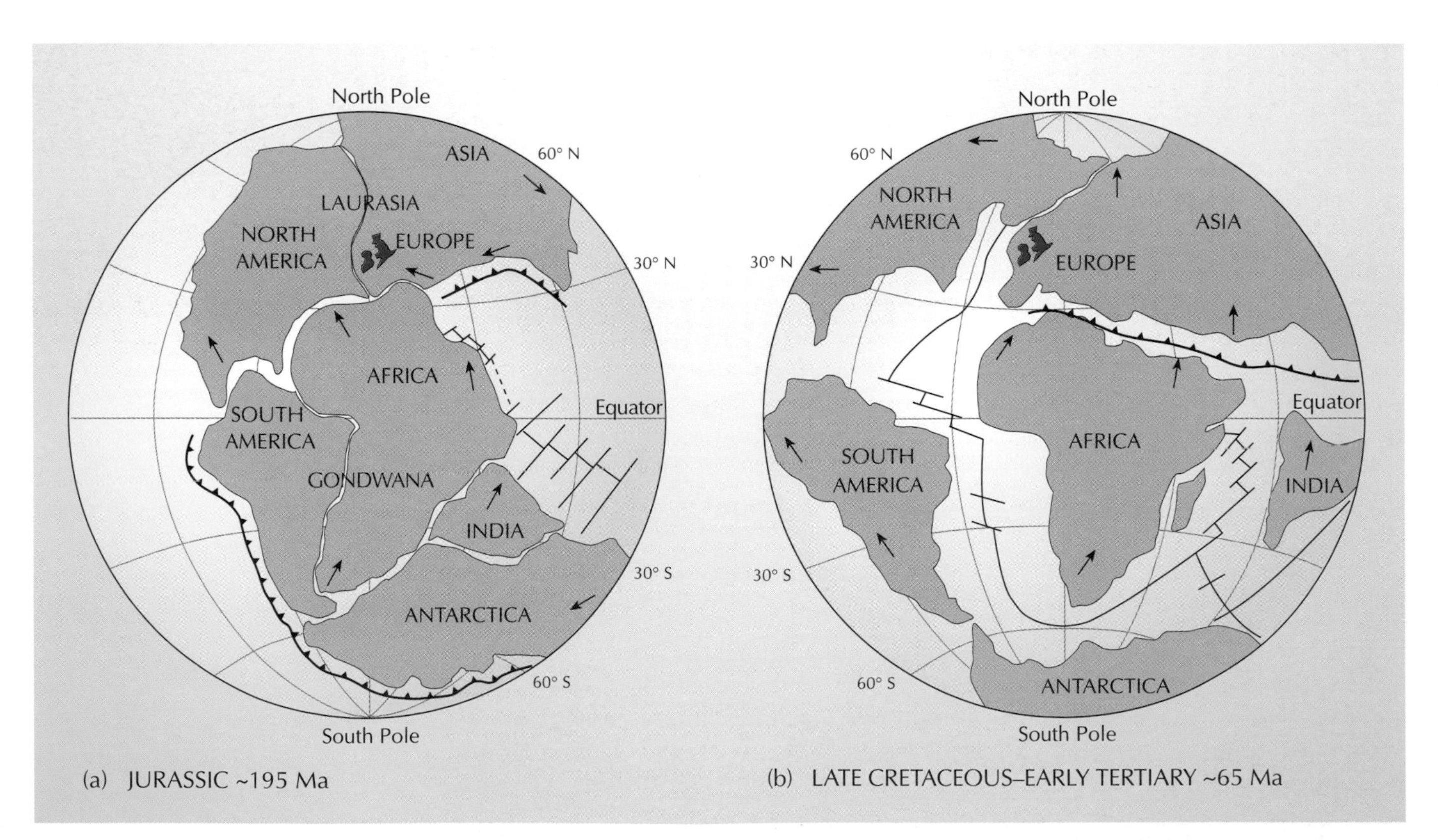

Figure 4.14 The position of the continents in: (a) the Jurassic Period (~ 195 million years ago); and (b) the late Cretaceous Period (~ 65 million years ago).

Figure 4.15 A typical glacier flowing down a mountain.

Figure 4.16 A glacier calving icebergs into the sea.

As more and more snow fell on the continent, snow crystals on the bottom were crushed and turned into **glacial ice**. Over time, the Antarctic ice-sheet has grown to a thickness of several kilometres that covers most of the continent today.

- According to the *CIA World Factbook* (Box 4.2), what percentage of Antarctica is covered by ice?

- 98% of Antarctica is covered by ice (the remaining 2% being barren rock).

The ice-sheet that covers Antarctica is derived from snow and so is freshwater. Between the ice crystals is trapped part of the Earth's atmosphere from the time when the snow actually fell. Later in the course, you will discover that by studying this ancient atmosphere, climate scientists have reconstructed a history of our planet going back almost half a million years. They have determined that the inclination of the Earth has not always been at 23.5° S to the Sun (as in Figure 4.12), but has varied over the millennia.

Figure 4.17 A typical Antarctic iceberg.

As snow continues to fall on the continent and is turned to ice, the weight of this ice causes it to flow away from the higher, central part of the continent, towards the edges, in slow-moving ice rivers called **glaciers** (Figure 4.15). When the glaciers reach the edge of the continent, they flow off the land into the ocean and break off (Figure 4.16) to form **icebergs** (Figure 4.17). These icebergs, which are sometimes hundreds of metres thick, then drift with the ocean currents away from the continent. In some areas the ice from the glaciers does not break away and instead forms large, floating **ice-shelves** (Figure 4.18), which are still attached to the continent. The largest ice-shelves are the

Figure 4.18 The edge of an ice-shelf.

Filchner–Ronne Ice-Shelf in the Weddell Sea, and the Ross Ice-Shelf in the Ross Sea (Figure 4.4). The Ross Ice-Shelf was actually known as the 'Great Ice Barrier' in the 'heroic age', because virtually all ice-shelves appear as huge walls of ice rising up to 40 m above the ocean.

4.8 Conclusions

The discovery of Antarctica was, although comparatively late in human history, broadly similar to the discovery of other island systems such as Mauritius and St Helena: exploration was swiftly followed by exploitation. You have learned about the climate of Antarctica, but the implications of the knowledge you have gained go much deeper. If you were asked to find the mean temperature of Antarctica, could you now give a sensible answer? Later in the course, you will see that the idea of global mean temperature is critical to arguments about climate change. With respect to the Maldives and sea-level, the ice-shelves on the fringes of Antarctica are floating, and so displace the same weight of water as they contain. The collapse of part of the Larsen-B Ice-Shelf, shown so dramatically in Figure 4.6, had no immediate effect on sea-level. In contrast, the ice-sheets that cover the continent are freshwater. If they melted these would provide *extra* water to the oceans and so raise sea-level. The Maldivians are quite right to be concerned about what may happen. These issues are covered in more detail later in the course.

In the next two chapters, we will consider the Antarctic ecosystem and see how Antarctica was globalized. We will also see how the method of governance that has been developed is designed to cope with both sustainability and uncertainty.

4.9 Summary of Chapter 4

4.1 Human contact with the Antarctic is very recent. Once humans had discovered Antarctica there was a rush of expeditions southwards from the 19th-century colonial powers.

4.2 Apart from the Antarctic Peninsula, Antarctica is roughly circular, centred approximately on the South Pole with an area about the same size as Europe. A polar projection map of the Antarctic is centred on the South Pole, with lines of longitude radiating from the pole and lines of latitude shown as concentric circles around the pole.

4.3 A Mercator projection map shows longitude as vertical lines and latitude as horizontal lines.

4.4 Several countries have made territorial claims in Antarctica but these are not recognized in International Law. Countries with territorial claims, plus several others, operate research stations in Antarctica, and these are mostly located on the coast.

4.5 The area of Antarctica is variable, depending on the area of ice-shelf attached to it, and different figures for the total area are given by different sources. About 98% of the continent is covered in ice.

4.6 When using the Internet to answer a question it is possible to avoid distraction and minimize time online by posing a carefully considered and focused question, deciding in advance what information is needed to answer the question, then going offline to evaluate the information and draw conclusions.

4.7 Air temperatures in Antarctica are dependent on the amount of incident solar radiation received and the amount of heat gained from the ocean. Antarctica is often thought of as having an extreme, unremittingly cold climate, but in fact it has a seasonal climate, with relatively mild summers on the coast. Inland areas have a shorter summer and a coreless winter.

4.8 Antarctica lay much closer to the Equator 195 million years ago, but continental drift has moved it to its present polar position. The thick sheet of glacial ice covering most of the continent probably developed within the last 20 million years. Glacial ice flows off the continent via glaciers and either remains attached to form a floating ice-shelf or breaks off at the edges to form icebergs.

Learning Outcomes for Chapter 4

Having completed this chapter, you should be able to:

4.1 Define and use, or recognize definitions and applications of, each of the terms given in **bold** in the text. (Questions 4.1, 4.2 and 4.9)

4.2 Discuss the history of Antarctic discovery. (Questions 4.3 and 4.5)

4.3 Recall and use facts about Antarctic geography and climate. (Questions 4.1, 4.2, 4.4–4.9)

4.4 Discuss and use strategies for finding information on the Internet. (Questions 4.10 and 4.11)

Questions for Chapter 4

Question 4.1

What are the main features of a coreless winter, and why would we not expect to see one on the coast of Antarctica?

Question 4.2

Why will the melting of an ice-shelf not affect sea level?

Question 4.3

Who discovered Antarctica?

Question 4.4

Why would you not draw a map of Antarctica on a Mercator projection? What type of map projection would you use?

Question 4.5

Which of the following countries have *not* made a territorial claim in Antarctica but operate research stations? (a) Chile; (b) Argentina; (c) Australia; (d) The United States; (e) France and (f) Britain.

Question 4.6

Why does the area of Antarctica change over time?

Question 4.7

What would the climate of Antarctica have been approximately 195 million years ago?

Question 4.8

Would you expect the warmest temperatures in Antarctica to be at the same time of year as those in the UK?

Question 4.9

What is the defining feature of glacial ice?

Question 4.10

Why should you be careful when looking for information on the Internet?

Question 4.11

Why is thinking carefully about what you want to find on the Internet desirable?

References

CARA (Center for Astrophysical Research in Antarctica) (2002) [online] Available from http://astro.uchicago.edu/cara/vtour/ant.cia.gif [Accessed 8 November 2002]

Cherry-Garrard, A. (1922) *The Worst Journey in the World.* Constable and Co. Reprinted 1994, London: Macmillan.

Hough, R. (1994) *Captain James Cook.* London: Hodder and Stoughton.

Mickleburgh, E. (1987) *Beyond the Frozen Sea.* London: Paladin.

Sullivan, W. (1957) *Quest for a Continent.* London: Secker & Warburg.

Stommel, H. (1984) *Lost Islands.* Vancouver: University of British Columbia Press.

World Flag Database (2002) [online] Available from http://www.flags.net/ [Accessed 10 June 2002]

World Factbook (2001) [online] Available from: http://www.bartleby.com/151/ [Accessed 27 November 2002]. The up-to-date version of the *CIA World Factbook* is available at: http://www.odci.gov/cia/publications/factbook/index.html [Accessed 27 November 2002]

Chapter 5 Perception and reality — the 'invisible' ecosystem

Prepared for the course team by Mark Brandon and Julian Priddle

5

5.1 Introduction

If the motivation for the discovery of Antarctica in the heroic age was well-publicized *exploration*, the voyages of *exploitation* that took place around the same time — for example the voyages of the sealers — were, by contrast, generally hidden from view. In this chapter we look at the ecosystem that these voyagers were exploiting to build up a picture of the true complexity of the natural environment. The Antarctic ecosystem is generally considered to be straightforward in that there are few animal species to consider. However, we need to understand what happens in this ecosystem in order to avoid repeating the events that happened on the islands of St Helena, Mauritius and Rapa Nui. Chapter 6 will set out the contemporary response to this question.

When you were asked to think about Antarctica in Chapter 4, did you consider the wildlife? It would not have been surprising if you had, given the resources that media organizations such as the BBC have thrown at the region. What you may not have realized is that media organizations tend to focus on the 'charismatic macrofauna' — that is, the animals that are large, easy to observe, and of course beautiful. In this chapter you will see that there is a lot more to the wildlife in Antarctica, and indeed in any region, than you may have realized. Our aim here is to understand the marine ecosystem in Antarctica because this supports the region's biological resources. In particular, you will see the contrast between the role played by large animals (macrofauna) at the top of the food web, and the tiny ones (microfauna) at the bottom. The main components of the Antarctic ecosystem are invisible beneath the waves, and the smallest organisms are the most important.

Throughout this chapter we are going to focus on the key course theme of uncertainty in a natural system. The marine ecosystem is strongly influenced by the physical environment through processes that have a variety of time and space-scales, from the turbulence and mixing caused by storms and ocean currents that act over periods ranging from days to years through to the thousands and millions of years of natural climate variations. But as you saw in the first part of this course, as well as being acted upon by external forces such as turbulence, natural systems have their own inherent variability.

To understand how its ecosystem has developed we must look at Antarctica's habitats. In the last chapter, you saw that Antarctica is an extreme environment. Although you may be aware that some species of wildlife are abundant, at least in some places, it is clear that Antarctica does not exactly provide an obvious habitat for living things. Humans can inhabit a huge variety of places, but to do this we use technology to extend our range — for example to go into space we need to take our environment with us in a space suit. Even so, much of Antarctica is at one extreme of the range of conditions where even adaptable humans can survive.

- Think back to the previous chapter. What contrasting views of Antarctica as a habitat were described?

- On the one hand Antarctica is a place where wildlife can be very abundant and diverse, for example with large penguin colonies. On the other hand, wildlife is sparse where the continent is covered with an ice-sheet that is kilometres thick.

The contradiction between these two views of Antarctica as a habitat is resolved quite easily. The biologically-rich picture is associated with the sea, the **marine ecosystem**; whilst the biologically-poor picture is that of the land, the **terrestrial ecosystem**. This distinction is not hard and fast — both systems are variable — but it is a useful generalization which will underpin the development of this chapter.

5.2 The Southern Ocean

Have you heard of the Roaring 40s or the Screaming 50s? They are the names given by the sailors to the winds that tear around the Southern Ocean. However, despite the extreme physical conditions, there really is plenty of life to be found in the region. In Chapter 4 you saw a map of the atmospheric temperatures around Antarctica (Figure 4.10). Earth-orbiting satellites can show us the global sea surface temperature (SST) in much greater detail (Figure 5.1).

- Large areas of the Southern Ocean in Figure 5.1 are coloured pink and purple. What do these colours indicate?
- Very cold surface temperatures. The mauve colour represents a temperature of ~4 °C, so the areas coloured pink are colder than this.

The boundary between the cold southern waters and warmer northern waters is called the **polar front**. South of the polar front, the sea surface temperature (SST) only changes

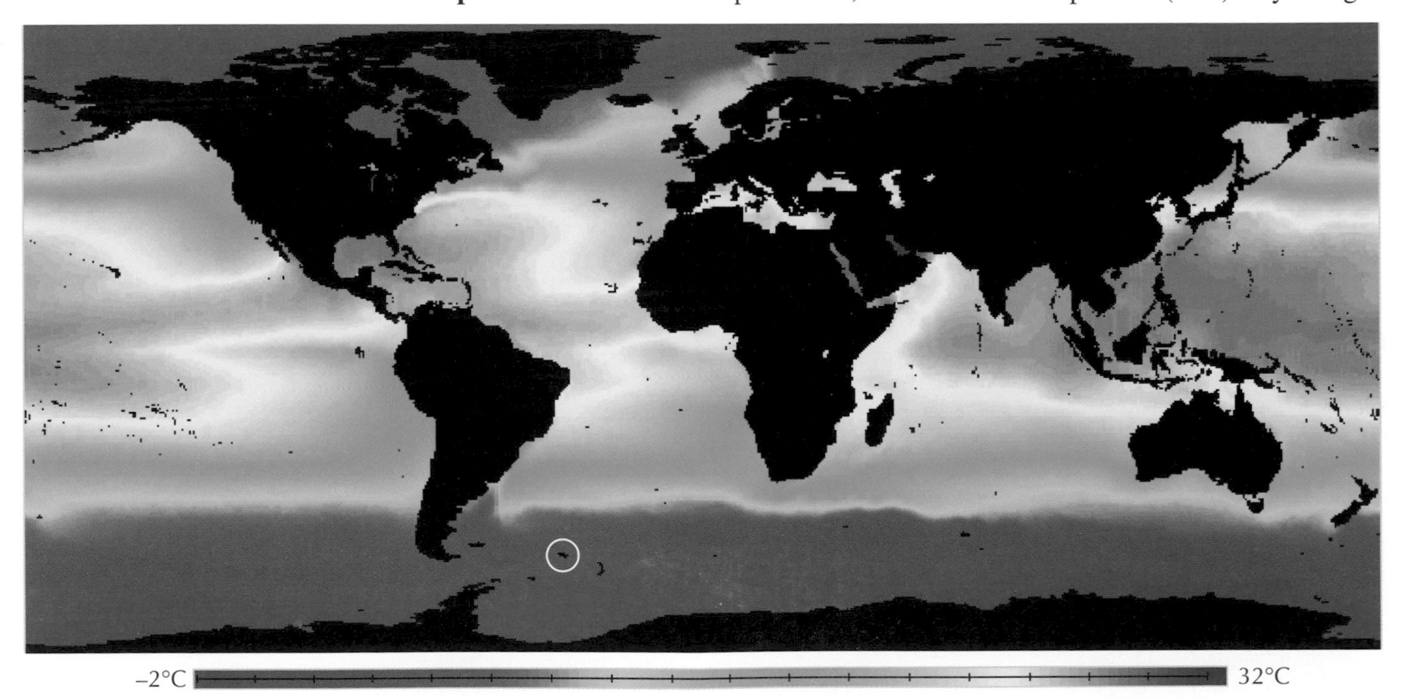

Figure 5.1 A global sea surface temperature map. Different temperatures are shown as different colours and the range is from −2 °C to 32 °C. This image is actually the annual mean picture, but data for individual weeks can be downloaded from the Internet. South Georgia is circled.

by about 4 °C all the way to the Antarctic continent, but to the north the SST increases very rapidly (from dark blue to green) by about 10 °C in a very short distance. The relatively uniform SST water south of the polar front makes up part of what is called the **Antarctic Circumpolar Current** (ACC). This current circulates in a clockwise direction around Antarctica and, although slow, the volume of water moving is tremendous — roughly 100 000 000 m^3 of water passes through the Drake Passage every second.

In the previous chapter, you learned that the ocean keeps the Antarctic coast relatively warm in winter (Section 4.6.3). However, it can also keep places cold. Captain Cook was surprised that South Georgia was covered in ice and snow when, at 54° S it is not so far from the Equator (Section 4.2) — after all, the British Isles are roughly the same distance from the Equator at 53° N and so both areas should receive roughly the same amount of solar radiation.

- Looking at Figure 5.1, why do you think the island is so cold?
- South Georgia is south of the polar front and is surrounded by relatively cold water that affects the climate to such an extent that the island is almost as cold as the Antarctic itself.

If solar radiation were the only factor determining climate, South Georgia and the British Isles ought to be very similar, but clearly they are not. The Gulf Stream is a warm ocean current that originates in the Gulf of Mexico and travels northeast across the Atlantic. It flows past the British Isles keeping them warmer than expected. By contrast, the cold waters of the ACC keep South Georgia cold and heavily glaciated.

So if the waters around Antarctica are cold, and these can have a tremendous impact on the climate of other regions, let us think about what happens when the Southern Ocean freezes. Large areas of the ocean are below 0 °C (Figures 4.10 and 5.1). However, the ocean does not freeze at 0 °C because water containing dissolved salt has a lower freezing point than freshwater. The temperature at which seawater freezes is dependent on the concentration of salt, but is usually about –1.8 °C. Large areas around the Antarctic continent have air temperatures below this. Using Figure 4.10 you can estimate how much of the ocean would freeze in a typical winter and stay frozen in the following Antarctic summer.

Satellites can also map the areas of ice on the surface of the ocean, as shown in Figure 5.2 (overleaf). Each coloured dot that makes up the picture represents the mean percentage ice cover over a whole month for an area of about 20 km^2. For example, a value of 50% ice cover means that half of the area (10 km^2) is covered in sea-ice, and the other half is open water. As you probably predicted from Figure 4.10, the area of sea-ice is much smaller in summer than it is in winter.

- Why would global warming change the area of sea-ice?
- As atmospheric temperatures increase over the whole planet, colder air would cover less of the ocean, so the area of sea-ice would decrease.

- Comparing the area of sea surface temperatures lower than –1.8 °C shown in Figure 4.10a, with the area of summer sea-ice in Figure 5.2a, there is less ice than you would predict. Why would this be the case?
- Figure 4.10 shows mean sea surface temperatures over the whole summer, whereas Figure 5.2 shows the amount of sea-ice for the single month of February,

i.e. in the middle of summer when temperatures are higher than the average for the whole summer.

You can add up the amount of ice represented by each coloured dot in Figure 5.2 to find out the *total* amount of Antarctic sea-ice in the Southern Hemisphere over several years (Figure 5.3a) and by taking the mean of each month's data for the whole time series, you can work out the mean cycle of ice area aound Antarctica (Figure 5.3b).

You can see that there is the strong annual cycle that you would expect. In winter the area of sea-ice is at a maximum, and in the summer it is at a minimum. What is perhaps more surprising is the year-to-year variability, with more ice in some years and less in others.

- From Figure 5.3, what is the *minimum* area covered by sea-ice during this period, to the nearest million square kilometres?
- ~ 4 million km^2.

- What is the *maximum* area covered by sea-ice during this period to the nearest million square kilometres?
- ~ 19 million km^2.

- Recall the value given for the area of Antarctica in the *CIA World Factbook* (Section 4.4.2). How does the maximum area covered by sea-ice compare with the land area of Antarctica?
- The *World Factbook* stated that the area of Antarctica is 14 million km^2. The graph in Figure 5.3 shows that the area of sea-ice can be over 19 million km^2.

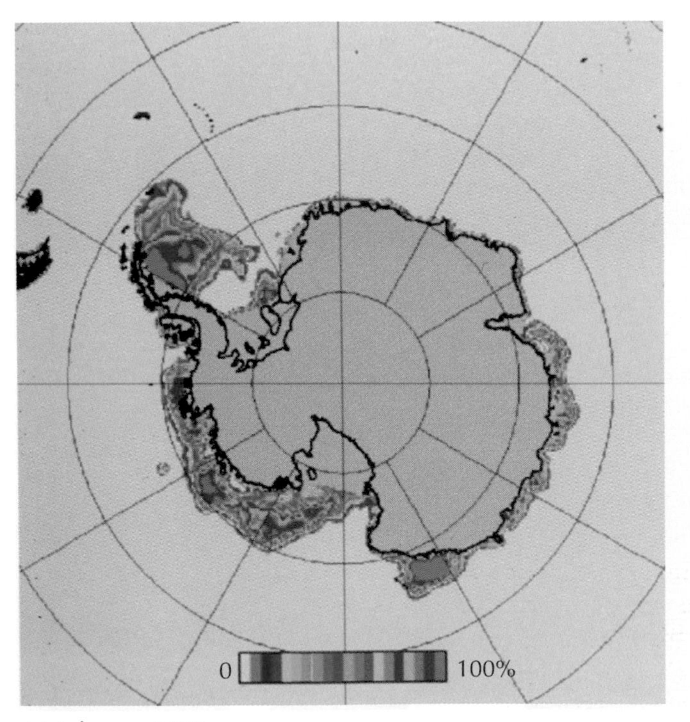

(a) February 1998

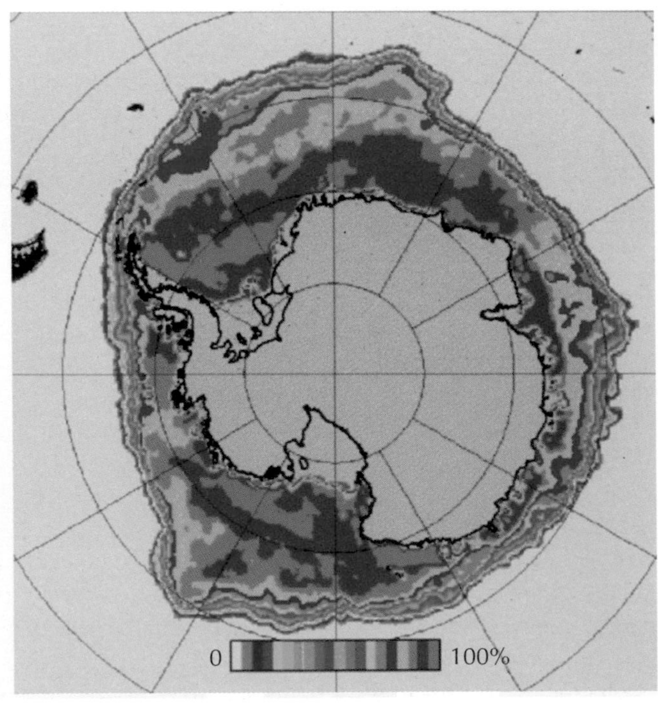

(b) September 1998

Figure 5.2 The typical sea-ice distribution around Antarctica — light blue represents open water. (a) February 1998 — Antarctic summer. (b) September 1998 — Antarctic winter.

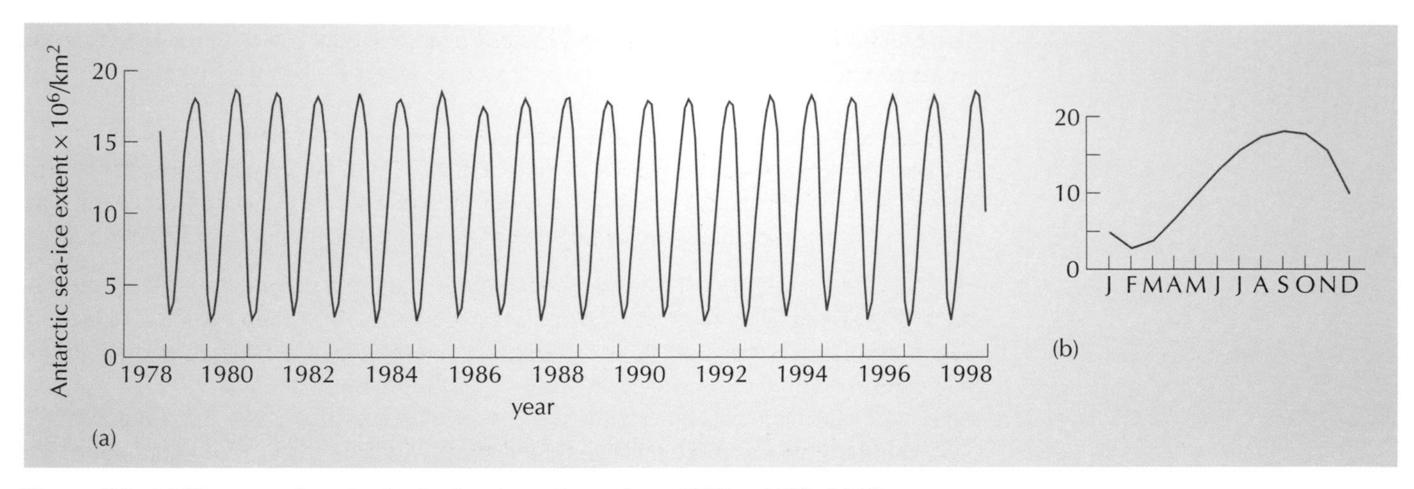

Figure 5.3 (a) The area of sea-ice in the Southern Ocean from 1978 to 1998. (b) The mean monthly area of sea-ice in the Southern Ocean.

$19 - 14 = 5$ million km^2

The sea-ice can cover up to 5 million km^2 more than the total area of Antarctica. So, in the southern winter, the area of Antarctica effectively more than doubles.

The winter maximum extent of sea-ice is absolutely vast, and this huge area of ice is a habitat for Antarctic wildlife such as penguins and seals. But where does the ice come from? Obviously it is made through the freezing of seawater. So, if we take a glass of water and mark the level on the side, freeze it and then allow the ice to melt, does the level of water in the glass change? If there were no other processes such as evaporation going on, the level of water would *stay the same* and this is what happens with seawater. So changes in the area of sea-ice do not affect sea-level. Sea-ice is, however, still important for climate because ice is a very good insulator and once present it prevents the ocean from further cooling. It also acts like a sponge. In the same way that atmospheric gases are trapped within the snow on the Antarctic continent (Section 4.7), seawater, and more importantly what is in the seawater, is trapped between ice crystals within the sea-ice. Later you will see that this trapping of water is critical for sea-ice as a habitat.

The fastest way for sea-ice to form is through what is called the frazil-pancake cycle. In this cycle, cold temperatures cool the surface of the sea down to the freezing point (−1.8 °C) and ice crystals called **frazil ice** form. Because ice is less dense than water, the crystals float and form a layer on the surface that looks very similar to an oil slick (Figure 5.4a, overleaf) and which is sometimes called 'grease ice'. The ice crystals dampen the higher frequency waves and so within the area covered by the ice it is calmer. This can be seen in Figure 5.4a — outside the ice slick there are breaking waves, but inside there are not. As it gets calmer the ice crystals stick together to form small plates (Figure 5.4b) that are rounded by constantly bumping into each other — this is called **pancake ice** — and the bumping creates raised edges (Figure 5.4c). As more seawater freezes, more wave energy is dampened and the pancakes grow up to 3 m in diameter. Eventually the pancakes freeze together and are piled up on top of each other by storms to form larger ice floes. Water freezes onto the bottom, and snow falls on the surface of these large floes, increasing their thickness to an average of about 1.5 m. Large areas of this ice are called **pack ice** (Figure 5.4d). Figure 5.3 shows that the change in ice area from summer to winter is relatively slow. When the sea-ice melts and retreats, the process is not the reverse of Figure 5.4. Instead the ice floes break up into small floes and then decay by melting very rapidly into water.

You should now go to the CD-ROM associated with this book and view the video on sea-ice formation and decay.

5.3 Antarctic habitats

By now you should be aware of the kind of environmental conditions that animals in the Antarctic have to contend with, and these characteristics are summarized in Box 5.1. Although we know why Antarctica is cold, why it is ice covered, and about the variability of the sea-ice, none of this explains why there is such a dramatic contrast between the Antarctic land ecosystem and the Antarctic marine ecosystem.

The sparse terrestrial ecosystem results from a combination of biogeographical isolation, low and often widely fluctuating temperatures, and drought. By contrast, the marine ecosystem is almost benign.

Figure 5.4 The frazil–pancake cycle showing the most rapid method of growth of Antarctic sea-ice: (a) frazil ice forming a 'slick' on the sea surface; (b) pancake ice; (c) pancake ice with raised edges; (d) pack ice.

Box 5.1 Antarctic conditions for life

We can think of an ecosystem as a community of animals, microbes and plants plus their physical environment. The conditions of this environment are, of course, fundamental to the life found in it.

Temperature

It takes more heat to raise the temperature of water than it does for air or rock. This means that the temperature of the ocean fluctuates only very slightly — much of the Southern Ocean falls within a 2–4 °C range, just above freezing point (Figure 5.1). However, on land, temperatures can plummet to below −50 °C in winter, whereas a clump of moss on a bare rock could rise to +30 °C on a sunny summer day. So, not only can the land be colder, but it also has a much more variable temperature regime.

Water

With about 90% of the planet's non-marine water contained in the Antarctic ice cap, it is not obvious that water availability is a problem for living organisms. However, water is only biologically useful as a liquid. Inland Antarctica is a cold desert, where conditions mimic the freeze-drying process used to preserve foodstuffs. Water availability is of course not a problem in the ocean.

Geography

As the continents drifted apart (Figure 4.14), South America was the last land mass to part company with Antarctica as the Drake Passage opened up some 20 million years ago (before the present cycle of ice ages and interglacial periods). It then became impossible for large organisms to migrate from warmer climates into Antarctica, and large animals that remained died out and can be seen as part of the fossil record. The land ice then restricted life to a few limited oases, which made colonization within the continent difficult. No such physical barriers exist in the ocean.

Suitable habitats are limited on land, and large animals are absent. The terrestrial ecosystem is composed of only two flowering species of simple plants, mosses and lichens, and small invertebrate animals. These organisms are adapted to the incredibly harsh conditions of sub-zero temperatures, a large temperature range, long periods of darkness, and low water availability. In fact, the terrestrial ecosystem is probably similar to what you expected from your knowledge of the Antarctic environment before you began studying this book. Despite these extreme conditions, life can survive in the most unlikely places. For example, one area of continental Antarctica in Southern Victoria Land is known as the 'Dry Valleys', because unusual meteorological conditions have kept them snow- and ice-free for millions of years. The valleys seem totally devoid of life and there are even mummified seals that have accidentally migrated inland from the coast and subsequently been freeze-dried. Yet, in amongst all this sterility, a microbial ecosystem survives by colonizing the spaces between crystals in coarse sandstone — this is known as an **endolithic** community (Figure 5.5, overleaf).

The marine ecosystem is very different. Marine wildlife, especially birds and mammals, form one of the major tourist attractions in the region. Even if you are aware that not

Figure 5.5
A photomicrograph of an endolithic community living within sandstone from the Antarctic Dry Valleys.

all areas boast such spectacular 'eco-tourism assets', it is clear that the Southern Ocean ecosystem is not subject to quite such extreme conditions as the land. But how does this ecosystem compare with others? To take the African bush as an example of another eco-tourism venue with 'charismatic macrofauna', is it possible to describe the two in a way which allows valid comparison? Indeed, what is being compared? We have already used words such as 'rich' and 'diverse', but these are not easy to quantify — especially when considering such key issues as uncertainty and sustainability.

To introduce ecosystems, we will compare those of the African bush and the Antarctic marine environment.

5.4 Ecosystems from top to bottom: leopards and leopard seals

Whether in the African savannah or the Southern Ocean, ecosystems share some fundamental similarities. Most fundamental of all to the concept of an ecosystem is the idea that its parts are *connected* by the transfer of carbon and other chemical elements. It all starts with plants or algae, which acquire their carbon from CO_2 in the environment. Thereafter, materials are transferred whenever a predator feeds upon prey, up the **food chain**, to the **top carnivores**. Each step in the chain is called a **trophic level** and much energy is dissipated with each transfer to a higher level. The top carnivores are often charismatic predators such as leopards in the savannah and leopard seals in the Antarctic, animals that have become icons for their respective regions (Figure 5.6). Because these animals sit at the highest trophic level in each ecosystem, a comparison between their biology will tell you a great deal about the similarities and differences between the two ecosystems they inhabit.

The leopard (Figure 5.6a) is a big cat that inhabits a variety of habitats in Africa and feeds on a range of other mammals — mostly what we would consider to be medium-sized **herbivores** such as gazelles. These herbivores in turn feed on large plants, especially the grasses of the surrounding savannah. In ecosystem-speak, the plants are called **primary producers**. The leopard seal (Figure 5.6b) is an equally spectacular Antarctic predator (although it can range as far north as New Zealand). Although slightly bigger than a leopard, it differs in that leopard seals don't normally eat herbivores — their diet is predominantly penguins and other seals, which are themselves **carnivores** — and they are associated with, and breed on, pack ice (Section 5.2).

(a)

(b)

Figure 5.6 (a) A leopard (*Panthera pardus*) in the African savannah. (b) A leopard seal (*Hydrurga leptonyx*) on Antarctic sea-ice.

- Name the trophic levels we have so far mentioned, starting at the bottom of the food chain.

- Primary producers → herbivores → carnivores → top carnivores.

If we look at pictures of the two iconic top carnivores, we realize that they highlight a major distinction between the two habitats, one that is not so much about a difference between tropical and polar, as between land and sea. One thing that leopards do well is climb trees — they can even do this while carrying prey, such as a gazelle. The tree is a large plant that forms part of the baseline trophic level of the ecosystem and provides food for some of the leopard's prey, but it also forms part of the physical fabric of the ecosystem, enabling the leopard to avoid larger predators. Now go back to the leopard seal. Where are the plants and where are the equivalent of gazelles? The simple answer is that you wouldn't normally notice them. The marine 'gazelles' are small invertebrate animals similar to prawns. The marine equivalent of the grasses are tiny single-celled algae, called **phytoplankton**, which are invisible to the naked eye.

5.5 The 'grass of the sea'

Carbon enters virtually all food webs through the photosynthetic activity of green plants or algae. These primary producers use sunlight as an energy source to synthesize complex carbon compounds using carbon dioxide and water as raw materials. Animals cannot do this, so they either have to eat plants or other animals. In the open ocean, most plants and algae are microscopic and drift in the upper few tens of metres of the surface waters. These algae (Figure 5.7a, overleaf) are single-celled and also occur in other aquatic habitats, and even on damp surfaces such as wet walls. The algal cells in the ocean drift with the currents, forming part of the community called the **plankton**. The word plankton comes from the Greek word for 'drifting' and the term **phytoplankton** refers to the algae in the plankton — you will meet zooplankton, their animal counterparts later.

An oak tree weighing hundreds of tonnes and a single phytoplankton cell 25 μm across and weighing half a nanogram (0.000 000 000 5 g) will fulfil exactly the same productive

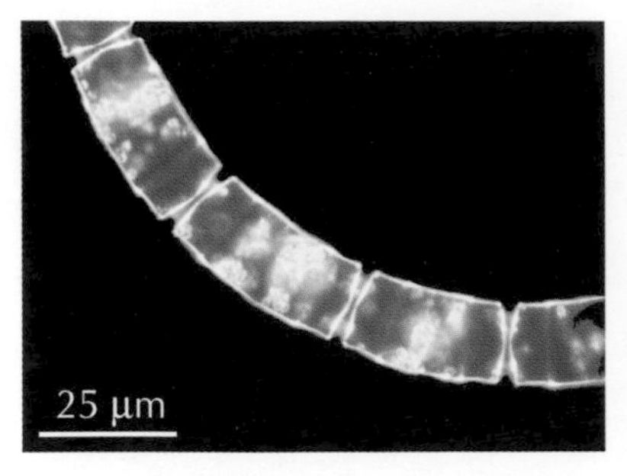

(a)

(b)

Figure 5.7 (a) A photomicrograph of a plankton *Odontella*, which is made up of several cells. (b) An ocean colour image from the SeaWiFS sensor on the SeaStar satellite.

function in their respective ecosystems. They both need light to grow — the oak tree invests much of its **biomass** into a huge trunk so that it can grow above other plants and expose its leaves to as much sunlight as possible (biomass means literally mass of biological material). But the oak tree's strategy simply won't work over most of the ocean. The light needed for plants to grow only penetrates to about 100 m depth in the ocean, and the average ocean depth is approximately 3.8 km. There is no place for a deepwater oak tree and so other plants have evolved to fill the ecological niche.

Individual phytoplankton cells are not visible to the naked eye, but by collecting samples of water and then filtering out the algae we can count individual phytoplankton cells with a microscope. However, this is tedious work, and you could not be certain that one small sample was representative of the water around it. The phytoplankton cells contain the green pigment **chlorophyll**, which enables them to photosynthesize. This pigment also colours the water, and so offers a convenient way of detecting phytoplankton from ships, aircraft or even from space. Some satellites, for example SeaStar, are fitted with special sensors that can detect chlorophyll at the ocean surface. An image from the SeaStar satellite, collected using the SeaWiFS instrument (Sea-viewing Wide Field-of-view Sensor), is shown in Figure 5.7b. A global data set can be collected by this instrument every few days.

- We have said the satellite measures the colour of the ocean. However, what do you notice about the colours on the map in Figure 5.7b?

- The colours are not true-to-life. They are false colours used to represent values of chlorophyll concentration, much as colours are used to code for height on some contour maps. Blue colours represent low chlorophyll concentrations and red very high chlorophyll concentrations.

In contrast to oak trees, the microscopic phytoplankton cells don't need to build complex structures to out-compete other algae. This means that they can grow quite fast — cells can divide as often as once a day. Although this might not seem particularly fast, if you start with a mental picture of a single cell, double it after one day, double each of these the next day, and double all four resulting cells a day later, and so on, you soon get an idea of how quickly the population is growing. This sort of relationship between numbers of cells and time is called an exponential increase, and when plotted on a graph produces a shape like that shown in Figure 5.8. As the population of cells increases, so the rate of production of new cells increases, as they too contribute to the growth. The graph in Figure 5.8 predicts that, if you had one cell on day one, by the end of one month there would be 2^{30} cells! (i.e. 2 multiplied by itself thirty times). 2^{30} is a very big number (there are only about 2^{23} people on the planet), and this number is what you would get from just one cell. A litre of seawater typically contains a million (10^6) algal cells, so it would seem that there is the potential to generate huge amounts of phytoplankton. In theory, that million cells would become 535 million million cells (about 1000 times the global human population) after one month, and would weigh more than 20 kilograms. Left for only another two and a half months, you could have a weight of phytoplankton equal to that of the Earth.

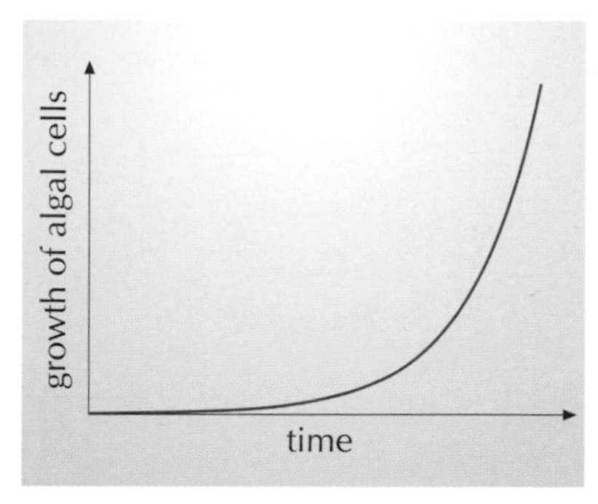

Figure 5.8 Exponential growth of algal cells.

Although in theory phytoplankton can grow this fast, in practice they obviously do not. Factors that prevent this exponential growth include a requirement for a constant supply of sunlight, CO_2, water and minerals such as nitrogen, phosphorus and iron for continued growth. Minerals are in scarce supply in some parts of the ocean. In addition the phytoplankton are eaten by herbivores.

- Can you identify a region in Figure 5.7b where the minerals essential for growth could be in short supply in the oceans?

- The areas that are dark blue, since they represent a low concentration of chlorophyll.

Figure 5.7b tells us that oceanic vegetation is not evenly distributed. The regions that are colour-coded red and orange signify a high abundance of phytoplankton and you could suggest that these areas are places where conditions are suitable for phytoplankton growth, perhaps because of a good supply of the extra mineral salts that the algae need. The areas colour-coded blue and purple have low abundance, and growth conditions are less favourable.

Phytoplankton cells die for a number of reasons, including viral infection and failure to get enough light to survive. A diverse range of grazing animals (herbivores) feed on both living and dead phytoplankton cells. The herbivores of the ocean are very efficient, and they keep the phytoplankton population at a steady level. In the Antarctic marine ecosystem, one of the most important grazers is a shrimp-like animal commonly known as 'krill'.

5.6 Krill — an 'invisible' herbivore

In the previous section we noted that the marine ecosystem did not have conspicuous herbivores. This does not mean that they do not exist. Krill are one of the most important consumers of phytoplankton in many parts of the ocean around Antarctica. There are several species but the most common is *Euphausia superba*, which grows up to 5–6 cm long when adult (Figure 5.9, overleaf). Although a great deal smaller than a gazelle, or any other mammal, krill are quite large by marine herbivore standards, where most of the grazing animals range in size from fractions of a millimetre up to a few millimetres. They tend to be carried along by currents and turbulence in the oceans, and together with their single-celled algal food source, form part of the plankton. Animal plankton are collectively known as **zooplankton**, but not all of them are herbivorous — even krill can graze successfully on other small zooplankton.

As a biological 'rule of thumb', small animals are energetic, fast growing and short-lived, whilst big ones tend to be a bit slower but live longer — for a comparison think

Figure 5.9 Antarctic krill (*Euphausia superba*) — the 'invisible' herbivore.

of a small scurrying mouse and a lumbering elephant. The small herbivores in the oceans would be expected to feed and grow rapidly. This means that they can respond very quickly to an increase in phytoplankton, and so the phytoplankton and grazer populations go through very similar cycles as the amount of phytoplankton changes. As the numbers of phytoplankton increase, the grazers multiply in the face of a food 'surplus', and so are very effective in the control of phytoplankton abundance.

A krill is quite a large zooplankton, and it is substantially larger than the phytoplankton on which it feeds. For example, if you magnified both organisms 1000-fold, an average alga would be about the size of a squash ball, whilst the krill would be the length of a small bus. Not surprisingly krill are abundant in the parts of the Southern Ocean with a dense food supply — that is of course large numbers of phytoplankton. Cynthia Tynan (1998) investigated the relationship between these large-scale patterns of distribution of the different trophic levels in the Southern Ocean (Figure 5.10). Figure 5.10a is an ocean colour map of phytoplankton production in the Southern Ocean derived from data collected over a period of about a year in the 1990s, and so is an average. The second image (Figure 5.10b) is a distribution map of catches of krill, based largely on data collected using large nets and over several years from a pioneering study of the Antarctic marine ecosystem in the 1930s called the Discovery Investigations. (We will hear more of this study in Chapter 6.)

The two maps certainly show that there is a similarity between the distribution of krill and its main food supply. However, these data sets should be treated with caution. Before we can draw any firm conclusions, we must be sure that the data sets are comparable.

- What features of the data might reduce the reliability of the comparison?

- There are uncertainties associated with each map. The process of averaging data over long periods of time introduces uncertainty, especially where spatial coverage is poor and uneven. There is also uncertainty in comparing two datasets that are collected by very different techniques and subjected to different averaging processes. Perhaps most importantly, the data were collected more than 50 years apart.

Analysis of ecosystem data interweaves environmental and biological variability — we call this patchiness — in both space and time. On top of this there is an uncertainty in all of the quantities we measure. It is difficult to completely understand an ecosystem.

The distribution of krill is not just patchy on the very large scales covered by Figure 5.10b. Krill are zooplankton and are carried along in the Antarctic Circumpolar

Current. However, they can also swim strongly enough to control their position relative to each other over distances up to tens of metres. In the same way that wildebeest form herds on the African savannah, krill are commonly found in large groups called 'swarms' that can range from tens of metres to a kilometre or more across, and they can move coherently like fish schools. Inside one of these swarms, there may be more than a thousand animals per cubic metre of seawater, although they are not permanent groups and they can disperse and re-form on time-scales from hours to days. The swarms can even change in size and shape from day to night, with krill forming swarms near the surface at night and dispersing at depth during the day. Armed with this knowledge about the behaviour of krill, you can immediately see why comparing data such as those in Figure 5.10 is a problem. To find out more about the marine ecosystem, we need to know how much krill is living there — in other words, we need a value for krill biomass.

- Can you see any potential problems with deriving krill biomass using nets to catch krill?

- The problem is how to get an accurate value for the krill numbers — and hence biomass. Because of the patchy distribution, if you only take a few samples you could go through the middle of a krill swarm, or even miss it altogether. This would greatly affect your overall answer for the biomass.

Until recently, nearly all sampling of life in the oceans involved catching organisms with various nets and other sampling devices. This method has been compared to using a helicopter above the clouds to sample life on land — you cannot see what you are fishing for, or how representative it is of the local ecosystem. To increase confidence in our data on krill we could take more measurements. If, for example, you were to take thousands of net samples, then you might be confident that you have sampled

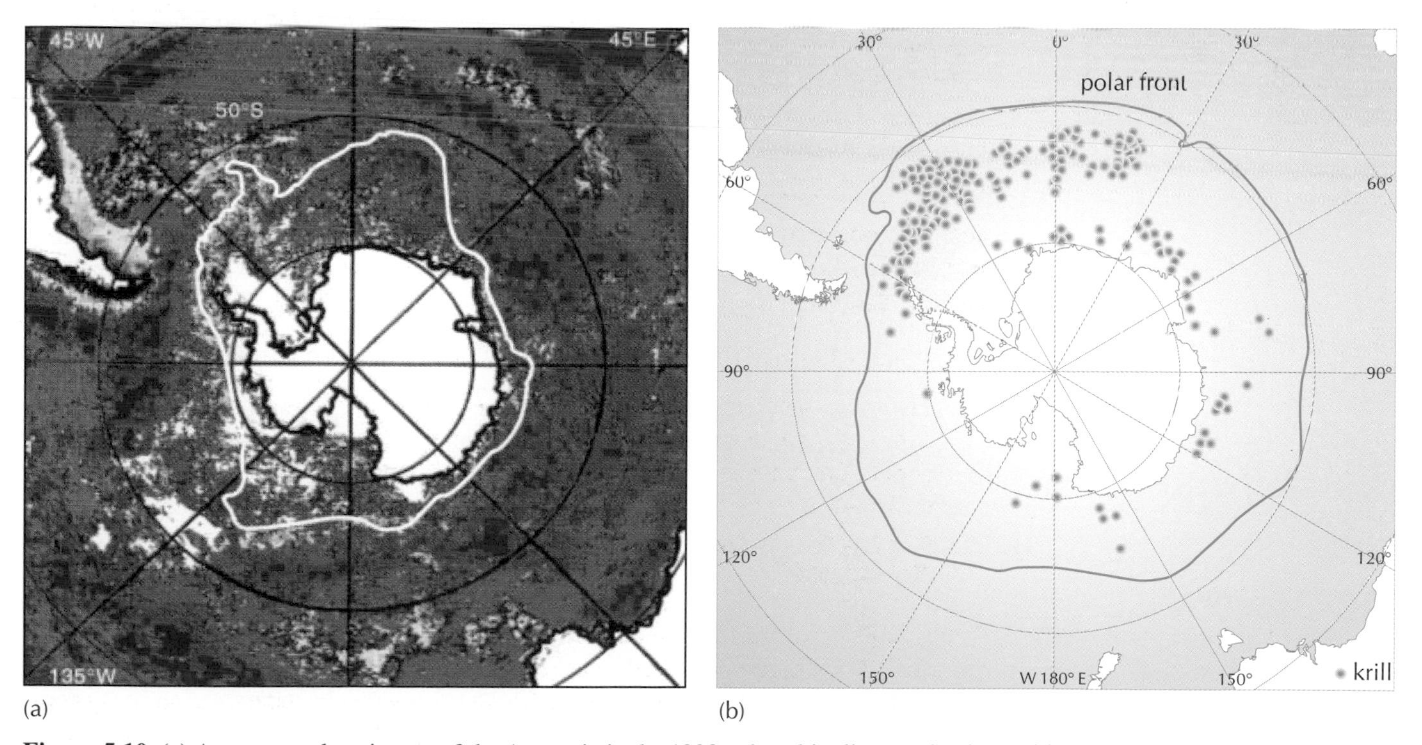

Figure 5.10 (a) An ocean colour image of the Antarctic in the 1990s; the white line marks the position of a minor ocean front. (b) The distribution of krill caught using nets in the 1930s; the blue line represents the position of the polar front.

a larger proportion of the total krill population, and so smoothed out the natural variability (or patchiness) in the system. Today, echo sounders in ships are used to routinely measure the amount of krill in the water as a ship moves along (Figure 5.11). This method gives a very high resolution picture of the krill abundance — but of course, only beneath the ship. So, it still does not come close to the spatial coverage of satellite data, such as those shown in Figure 5.10a.

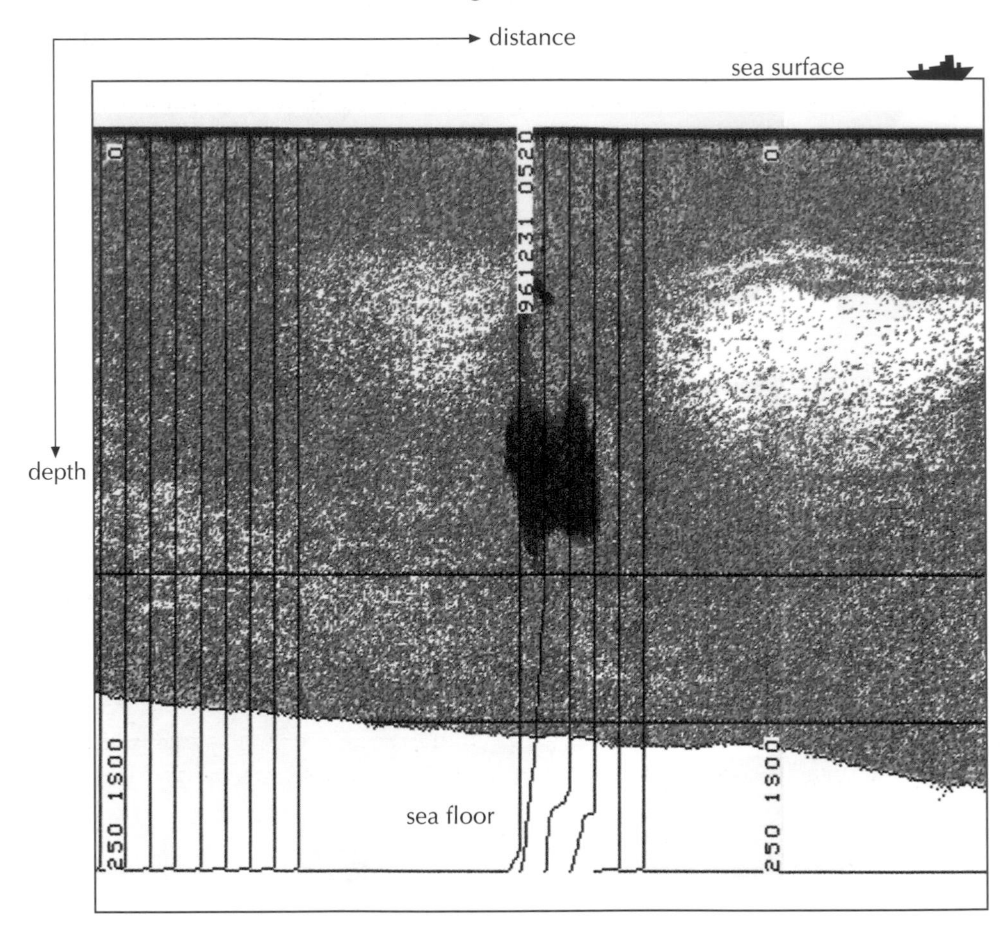

Figure 5.11 An echo sounder trace showing a krill swarm. The ship moves from left to right and the colours represent the amount of krill in the water column. The red-brown patch in the centre of the picture is a krill swarm.

If this swarming behaviour is a nightmare for biologists trying to quantify krill in the ecosystem, it is a heaven-sent opportunity for many of the animals that feed on krill, and in the next section we look at one such animal, the blue whale (*Balaenoptera musculus*).

5.7 The blue whale – a marine anteater?

Blue whales are probably the largest animals ever to have lived on the planet. Adults can be over 30 m long and weigh more than 100 tonnes. Paradoxically, they feed by filtering very small animals — zooplankton (such as krill) and fish — out of the water by taking a huge mouthful of water (Figure 5.12), and then straining out the animals using long fibrous plates called baleen, which hang down from the roof of their mouth. For a large blue whale, 'huge mouthful' means about 70 cubic metres of seawater — and that is more than half of the weight of the whale itself (a cubic metre of seawater weighs just over 1 tonne).

Just as there was a large contrast between the size of krill and phytoplankton, there is an equally impressive difference in size between whales and krill. If we return to our earlier size comparison where we increased organism sizes a 1000-fold, krill would be the size of a bus, whereas a blue whale would stretch from one end of the Isle of Wight to the other! Interestingly, the predator–prey size ratio is about the same as that between anteaters and ants. But even with the capacity to filter up to 70 tonnes of water in one go, blue whales could not feed on krill if they didn't occur in swarms. Biologists have estimated that a blue whale needs about 3 tonnes of krill per day to survive — this is about 3 million krill, at a gram each. Can you imagine how much effort this would take if krill were found in ones and twos? Blue whales — and several other large predators — can only exploit krill as their main food supply *because* swarming makes krill easy to catch in large numbers.

Figure 5.12 A blue whale feeding on a dense swarm of krill.

5.8 Production and biomass — putting some numbers into the ecosystem

To understand how this particular ecosystem functions, and perhaps to compare it with others, we need to follow the fate of phytoplankton material through the food web. As well as looking at biomass we must consider its increase (that is, production) and the efficiency of *transfer* between the trophic levels — the transfer is the ratio between the amount of food eaten, and the amount of production.

Blue whales need about 3 tonnes of krill per day to live. In an area with a very good food supply, krill can grow by 2–3% of their body mass per day; their growth rate slows as they approach their maximum size. For the whale's feeding to be sustained by krill production, it needs to forage over an area of the ocean which will yield 3 tonnes of krill per day.

- Assuming a mean krill growth rate of 2.5% of body mass per day, what biomass of krill is required to sustain one blue whale?

- Assuming a growth rate of 2.5% body mass per day:

  1 tonne of krill produces 2.5/100 = 0.025 tonnes of extra krill per day.

  To obtain 3 tonnes of *extra* krill body mass per day, we need:

  3/0.025 = 120 tonnes of krill.

This biomass of krill will typically occupy an area between 5 and 40 km^2 (depending on the local population density and number of swarms).

- If we assume that a 100-tonne blue whale eats 3 tonnes of krill per day, how long will it take for the whale to consume the equivalent of its own body mass?

- This will take:

  100/3 = 33.3 days,

  i.e. just over a month.

The krill will in turn need to eat more than 3 tonnes of phytoplankton to produce this amount of growth. In fact, the krill need about 25 tonnes of phytoplankton to produce 3 tonnes of biomass. By now you will be asking, what would be the mass of phytoplankton required for 25 tonnes of phytoplankton production, so that the system remains in balance.

- Given that typical daily phytoplankton production is about 20% of biomass, how much phytoplankton will be required to produce 25 tonnes per day?

- One tonne of phytoplankton produces:

  20/100 = 0.2 tonnes

  of extra phytoplankton per day at a growth rate of 20%. To get 25 tonnes of extra phytoplankton we need:

  25/0.2 = 125 tonnes

  in the study area.

We now have 'numbers' for the three trophic levels. In 5–40 km^2 of ocean, there is almost the same biomass of whale (100 tonnes), krill (120 tonnes) and phytoplankton (125 tonnes). The key to the food chain is the very different productivities at the three trophic levels. Phytoplankton grow fast — we have identified the daily production in our study area as 25 tonnes, or 20% growth. The production of krill in the same area was 3 tonnes at 2.5% growth. The whale would probably only gain 50–100 kilograms body mass per day — a growth rate of 0.0005–0.001%. Looking at trophic levels in terms of *productivity* rather than biomass (productivity is simply the rate of production) the pattern is clear: the system is remarkably inefficient at turning phytoplankton into whale biomass.

- If the whale really does eat 3 tonnes of food per day, but only builds up 50–100 kilograms of body mass, what has happened to the rest of the food?

- Some of the food that the whale eats, such as the exoskeleton of the krill, is indigestible, so it is lost as faeces.

Most of the food that passes through the gut wall of the whale is assimilated — but is then used as fuel to run the whale's muscles and other tissues, and provide the heat to maintain its constant body temperature.

Not a great deal of energy from primary producers appears in higher trophic levels, and birds and mammals are especially 'uneconomical' to run — typically accumulating only 2–4% of their food intake as production (compared with a figure of about 10% for cold-blooded vertebrates such as fish).

Turning 25 tonnes of phytoplankton into 0.1 tonne of whale blubber doesn't look all that impressive as a demonstration of efficiency. Nearly all the phytoplankton biomass has been used by the krill and whale to produce energy, or egested as faeces. Other, more complex food chains can be even less efficient. The 'alga-to-krill-to-whale' food chain involves only two transfers. Look at a leopard seal, eating a young Weddell seal which in turn fed on fish which ate krill.

- How many trophic levels are involved in this food chain?

- There are five trophic levels — three predators (leopard seal, Weddell seal and fish), a herbivore (krill) and primary producers (phytoplankton).

This food chain is more complex with an additional two trophic levels, and here only about 0.002% of phytoplankton biomass will be converted into new leopard seal biomass. Figure 5.13 shows a simple representation of the Southern Ocean food web, and you can see that food chains are typically quite short involving few trophic levels. It is also obvious that most of the arrows eventually reach or start from the krill. Where a single species plays a key role in an ecosystem, it is often termed a **keystone species**.

You can see from Figure 5.13 that the phytoplankton → krill → whale food chain is one of the simplest in the Antarctic. This comparatively efficient route for turning plant growth into mammal tissue involves a large, long-lived animal. The more complex trophic structures sustain a smaller biomass of top predators simply because there are greater energy losses as a result of the larger number of intermediate trophic levels.

Figure 5.7b showed that phytoplankton growth that sustains the ecosystem is typically quite low in the Southern Ocean. You can use this fairly moderate level of production to run 'expensive' predators such as whales *only* if you have a trophic structure that channels phytoplankton production efficiently to the top predators.

- What sort of food chains are most efficient at channelling the phytoplankton production efficiently to the top predators?

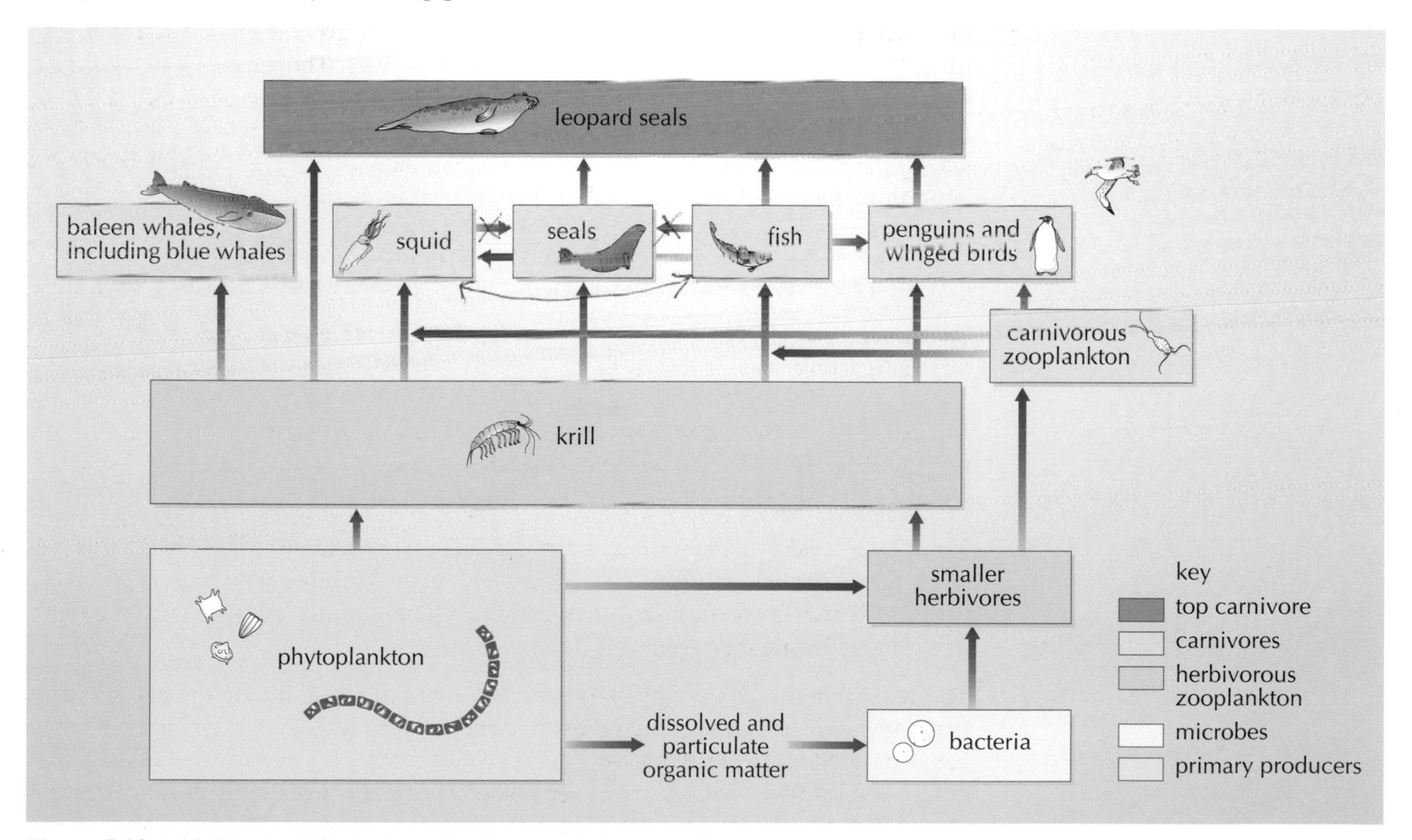

Figure 5.13 A highly simplified schematic diagram of the Antarctic open-ocean ecosystem, illustrating the importance of krill. Note that waste products from all the animals add dissolved and particulate organic matter to the water, which is fed upon by bacteria. Animals and microbes occurring in the sediment are not shown.

- Food chains with few trophic levels.

These short food chains are a dominant feature of the Southern Ocean (Figure 5.13) and work because of patchiness (Figure 5.11) — the krill feed on local phytoplankton hotspots and whales can only survive by feeding on krill because they occur in swarms. The Antarctic marine ecosystem is clearly not all that productive. Neither is it particularly diverse, despite the conspicuous predators such as whales, seals and penguins.

5.9 The ice–ocean ecosystem

So far, we have considered an open-ocean ecosystem. In Section 5.2 you saw that the Southern Ocean is covered by up to 19×10^6 km^2 of sea-ice at certain times of the year. What effect does this have on the ecosystem? If we again consider the simple phytoplankton ⟶ krill ⟶ whale food chain, how are these three organisms affected by sea-ice? For the phytoplankton, the most important effect is loss of light. Sea-ice is not clear like freshwater ice, and snow lying on the ice blocks out even more light.

- How would the decrease in light affect phytoplankton production?
- The phytoplankton need light to photosynthesize so we would expect a dramatic decrease in production.

At the other end of this particular food chain, sea-ice poses a major problem for whales and other air-breathing animals. If they cannot get to the surface, they cannot breathe. A dense sea-ice cover places the affected parts of the ocean off-limits for whales, so some species (such as the blue whales) migrate north to the tropics for the southern winter. Krill, on the other hand, are not affected directly by sea-ice. In fact, the nooks and crannies underneath older sea-ice provide a shelter where krill can hide from fish and other predators. But what are the krill eating?

If you look back to Figure 5.4a, the slurry of ice crystals traps anything suspended in the water — including phytoplankton. As the ice grows, there are many cavities and channels between the crystals that are rich in the chemicals needed for phytoplankton

Figure 5.14 Antarctic pack ice showing green–brown algae trapped in the sea-ice crystal matrix.

Figure 5.15 Crabeater seals basking on the Antarctic pack ice.

growth. Despite low temperatures and low light, some algal cells continue to grow within the sea-ice. Often the density of algae is so high that it can colour this sea-ice, though because these algal cells contain brown pigment that masks the green colour of the chlorophyll, the ice appears brown (Figure 5.14). So, krill also have a food supply in winter — they can graze on the algae trapped in the ice, and on the bottom of the sea-ice.

Far from being a hostile habitat, the sea-ice provides both food and shelter for krill. Other predators can also take advantage of the ice. The crabeater seal (*Lobodon carcinophagus*) spends its whole life cycle on the Antarctic pack ice (Figure 5.15) and, despite its name, lives on krill. Although you may not have heard of this species it is actually the world's most abundant seal, with an estimated population of 12 million living on the Antarctic pack ice.

5.10 Planet engineering with plankton

Concern over human impact on the global climate has led to a huge upsurge of interest in the mechanisms by which the biosphere influences the composition of the atmosphere. Later in the course, you will see that the concentration of CO_2 in the atmosphere is increasing, but this increase is just a by-product of a complex 'carbon cycle' that moves carbon around the planet. The IPCC stated that there are approximately 2000×10^9 tonnes of carbon stored on land, and approximately 730×10^9 tonnes stored in the atmosphere. In comparison, there is approximately $38\,000 \times 10^9$ tonnes of carbon stored in the oceans. Carbon dioxide is taken up by plants, including oceanic phytoplankton, and this constitutes what we call a carbon 'sink', helping to reduce the so-called greenhouse effect. However, other processes in the biosphere return some of this carbon to the atmosphere. To predict the impact of future climate changes, it is necessary to have an understanding of the balance between these biological 'sources' and 'sinks'.

Carbon dioxide is not thought to be a limiting resource for ocean phytoplankton. The limiting factors include elements such as nitrogen, phosphorus, silicon and sulfur that the phytoplankton require to build biomass. All of these nutrients are dissolved in seawater and removed by phytoplankton growth. In Figure 5.7b you saw that global plankton production (shown as ocean colour) does not occur uniformly, but interestingly, the oceans in some areas have high nutrient levels but low chlorophyll values. If there are high nutrient levels, what else is missing to prevent the phytoplankton growing? We have already identified some of the controls earlier in this chapter — lack of light, removal of phytoplankton by grazing and so on. There is now strong evidence that trace elements such as iron play a crucial role in algal growth. Iron is the most abundant element in the planet as a whole, but is only present in trace amounts in seawater. Experiments in laboratories and in the field have shown that the addition of dissolved iron to the environment of Southern Ocean phytoplankton, allows them to grow faster and to use up more of the available supply of other nutrients.

This raises an intriguing possibility. Would it be possible to 'seed' the Southern Ocean with iron and engineer a massive phytoplankton bloom? If this happened, would it remove some, or even all of the extra carbon dioxide which human activity has introduced to the atmosphere over the last century? John Martin, one of the scientists who originated the 'iron fertilization hypothesis', said:

> You give me half a tanker of iron, and I'll give you the next ice age.
>
> (cited in Kunzig, 1999)

Before you take this comment at face value, you should stop to think about some of the things that you have learned on this course. Would it be a feasible project? If it was, and phytoplankton production in the Southern Ocean increased to levels where it reduced the amount of carbon in the atmosphere, would all of this carbon be removed on a long-term basis? Would there be other implications for the marine ecosystem, and how would you go about assessing the various impacts that planetary engineering on this scale could involve? Finally, what legal and political framework exists to regulate such actions? These sorts of ideas are called mitigation and you will hear more of these in Book 3.

5.11 Conclusions

The Southern Ocean and the sea-ice are key components of the Antarctic ecosystem. Terrestrial life is as sparse as you would expect. In contrast, the ocean has an ecosystem with several conspicuous animal groups, which suggests that the region is biologically productive. However, large animals like whales can only survive if the food web is simple and consists of few trophic levels. Finally, the marine ecosystem may have the potential to reduce global warming.

5.12 Summary of Chapter 5

5.1 The Antarctic Circumpolar Current regulates and extends the Antarctic environment as far north as the polar front. The waters south of the polar front circulate clockwise around Antarctica.

5.2 The sea surface freezes at –1.8 °C, and sea-ice covers an area greater than the size of Antarctica in winter but less than a quarter of this area at the height of summer. The frazil–pancake cycle is the most rapid means of forming pack ice and seawater is trapped between the ice crystals.

5.3 Food webs consist of primary producers, herbivores, carnivores and top carnivores and these are structured into trophic levels.

5.4 The transfer of energy between trophic levels is very inefficient.

5.5 Plants and animals are not distributed uniformly across the Southern Ocean (or any other ocean), and physical factors such as ocean circulation play a major role in ecosystem variability.

5.6 Krill are the key Antarctic species and large predators can be supported as a result of their swarming behaviour.

5.7 The sea-ice around Antarctica is a component of the krill habitat.

5.8 Antarctic productivity may be limited by a lack of iron.

Learning Outcomes for Chapter 5

When you have completed this chapter you should be able to:

5.1 Define, illustrated by examples, and use appropriately the terms shown in **bold** in the text. (Questions 5.1–5.4).

5.2 Describe the formation and importance of sea-ice. (Questions 5.1, 5.3–5.5)

5.3 Describe, giving examples, ecosystem structure in the Antarctic. (Questions 5.2, 5.4, 5.6, 5.7)

5.4 Describe a possible method for mitigation of climate change. (Question 5.7).

Questions for Chapter 5

Question 5.1

In a few sentences describe and compare the climate of two islands, one on either side of the polar front.

Question 5.2

Assign the following animals to one of the trophic levels in the marine ecosystem:

(a) killer whale;

(b) penguin;

(c) krill;

(d) baleen whale;

(e) phytoplankton;

(f) crabeater seal.

Now draw a simplified food chain with five boxes to show the links between the trophic levels. Finally, state where humans would appear in this food chain.

Question 5.3

At which stage of sea-ice growth do the primary producers become entrained into the ice, and at which time of the year would you expect this to happen?

Question 5.4

In about 50 words, describe why you would not expect all sea-ice to contain a brown layer of chlorophyll.

Question 5.5

When sea-ice decays and retreats, what is the effect on sea-level?

Question 5.6

Why are animals such as the blue whale able to survive on krill?

Question 5.7

Why could the addition of iron to the Southern Ocean mitigate climate change?

References

Kunzig, R. (1999) *The Restless Sea*. New York: W. W. Norton and Company.

Tynan, C.T. (1998) Ecological importance of the southern boundary of the Antarctic circumpolar current, *Nature*, **392**, pp. 708–710.

6 Exploitation to the endgame: Antarctic governance

6

Prepared for the course team by Mark Brandon

6.1 Introduction

In previous chapters we discussed what happened once the pressures of globalization reached Antarctica in the 19th century. We noted the unregulated exploitation of its resources and the collapse of whole populations of marine mammals, together with the wider ecological repercussions of such decimation. We concluded that exploitation is only sustainable when it does not destroy the structure of the ecosystem which produces the harvest. In this chapter we will explore how governance of the resources in Antarctica has evolved to cope with exploitation.

Antarctica is a good region for this investigation because interventions have been generally well recorded as a result of the late arrival of humans on the scene. It provides a special case in the development of international governance, but it also deserves special attention because of the potential effect that events in Antarctica could have on the rest of the world as the climate warms up.

Politics and Antarctica had a quiet introduction. In 1908 the British Government made a claim for the Antarctic Peninsula from 20° W to 80° W, based upon the discoveries of previous British explorers (Table 4.1). Initially this claim seemed to go unnoticed on the international scene — but this was a time of great political upheaval in the western world and Antarctica was a long way away. However, it did not take long for other nations to become interested in the continent and its potential riches.

6.2 Exploitation continues apace

Whilst expeditions continued to explore Antarctica (Table 4.1), sealing continued until fur and elephant seal populations diminished to the point where it was no longer commercially profitable to send ships to South Georgia. At first sight, human predation upon seals was following a predator–prey cycle, but because predator numbers did not decrease as prey numbers fell, there was a massive population crash and seal numbers fell to such low levels that it was thought they may never recover. (Indeed, in 1958 a South Georgia survey showed that there were still fewer than 100 pairs of fur seals left. Their numbers have now risen to very high levels as you will discover later in this chapter.) However, there were other marine resources to exploit — the whales.

Returning to the voyages listed in Table 4.1, the Swedish South Polar Expedition led by Otto Nordenskjöld is one of particular note. The captain of Otto's ship, the *Antarctic,* was the Norwegian Carl Larsen and the expedition had a 'colourful' history. The ship was wrecked, and the expedition members and crew were rescued from the Antarctic Peninsula by the Argentinian Navy (the ship they used, the *Uruguay*, can still be seen in Buenos Aires). At the banquet to celebrate this rescue, Larsen said:

> I tank youse very mooch and dees is all vary nice and youse vary kind to mes, bot I ask youse ven I am here vy don't youse take dese vales at your doors, dems vary big vales and I seen dem in houndreds and tousands.
>
> (originally transcribed in 1903, quoted in Headland, 1984)

In the early 1900s, whales were used for a wide variety of purposes including food, lighting oil, and the manufacture of many things from soap to umbrellas to explosives. Larsen was a shrewd businessman and he knew that the output of northern European whaling stations was falling thus creating a gap in the market. With this in mind, he set up the Compañia Argentina de Pesca, with himself as whaling manager, and returned to Norway to fit out a whaling expedition. In 1904 he set off to South Georgia, an Antarctic region that he knew was particularly abundant in whales.

- Which country claimed ownership of South Georgia?

- Britain. Captain James Cook made the first landing and he claimed the island for Britain in January 1775.

Larsen set up a whaling station at a place he called Grytviken (Figure 6.1) on South Georgia (Norwegian for pot cove — the pots being those left by the sealers for boiling blubber), and his company paid a fee to the British Government for the use of the island, *and* for the whales they caught. The whaling fleet consisted of small, fast 'catcher' boats that harpooned whales and towed the carcasses to Grytviken for processing. In their first year the catcher boats barely had to leave the harbour to take humpback whales (*Megaptera novaeangliae*) and the slaughter began. That year Larsen took 236 whales made up of 189 humpbacks, 22 fin whales (*Balaenoptera physalus*), 17 blue whales (*Balaenoptera musculus*) and 7 right whales (*Eubalaena australis*). These whales provided a total of about 1250 tons of oil, although because of over-supply, the price of oil crashed to its lowest level ever (Jackson, 1978). This crash affected profits, but

Figure 6.1 Grytviken whaling station in the early 20th century. There is a blue whale on the flensing plan (the place where the blubber is stripped from the carcass). If you look closely at the middle left-hand-side of the picture, you should be able to see some pigs (feeding on blubber) that had been introduced to South Georgia.

Larsen persevered and the price of oil soon rose making the operation very profitable. With booming profits, whaling became an international industry in this region and within 10 years there were 10 operational shore-based whaling stations (Figure 6.1).

Setting up a whaling station in Antarctica was extremely expensive, but as the historian Gordon Jackson pointed out, there was a 'marriage of British resources and Norwegian labour ... that was the nature of "British" whaling for the rest of its life'. Norwegian was the language spoken at virtually all of the stations. But the situation took a strange twist when the first completely British whaling company — Salvesen's New Whaling Company — was prevented from setting up a South Georgia station by the British Colonial Office, which was trying to control the whaling. Jackson noted 'the incongruity of a British territory admitting foreigners and excluding Britons'. Eventually the British Government relented and Salvesen set up Leith whaling station in 1909. The impact of the rapidly developing industry and the vast catches were predictable, even without a complex understanding of the Antarctic marine ecosystem. An old northern whaler told one of the southern whalers in 1912:

> ... that they had better make hay while the sun shone, as if seven whalers were getting 7000 whales in one spot, it would not be very long before the southern whale fishery would follow the northern whale fishery, and the whales would practically disappear from the sea.
>
> (quoted in Jackson, 1978)

The real leap in technology that enabled whaling to continue when 'one spot' was fished out came with the introduction of the first factory ships in 1925. These ships allowed the industry to exploit whales at sea, where it was beyond the control of the British Government.

- Can you think of an obvious advantage in using factory ships?
- The factory ships allowed the small catcher boats to cover a much wider geographical area, and enabled the hunters to track the whales closely.

Huge factory ships operated all along the Antarctic Peninsula and they moored in sheltered coves to process the whales that were caught. However, the impact of the whalers was not solely on the marine ecosystem.

- What effect could the whalers be having on the land-based ecosystem?
- The introduction of non-native species.

The whalers deliberately introduced reindeer, cattle and pigs (you can see the latter feeding on whale blubber in Figure 6.1) to provide a varied diet. In the first part of this book, we saw that island ecosystems are vulnerable, and the introduction of a new species such as reindeer that could easily survive in the environment was immediate and significant. (There are still several hundred reindeer on the island (Figure 6.2, overleaf), although there are plans to remove them.) The whalers also accidentally introduced rats and mice. As on Lord Howe Island (Section 2.7), the rats have devastated local bird life. In fact, the geographical expansion of both the rat and reindeer populations across South Georgia has been limited only by their inability to cross the glaciers that cover the island.

Figure 6.2 Reindeer at one of the derelict whaling stations on South Georgia.

So, the British controlled much of the whaling in the Southern Ocean in the first half of the 20th century when the industry was based on South Georgia. But the people who worked at the whaling stations were British, Norwegians, Chileans and Argentinians. As the numbers of large whales began to drop, the industry shifted its targeted species to smaller animals. However, as catches fell, so did the revenue received by the British Government. The British Colonial Office was well aware of what was happening, and in a bid to prevent the total collapse of whale stocks it set up the first long-term Antarctic research programme. The programme was called The Discovery Investigations, named after the ship it was given (Captain Scott's ship from his 1901 expedition).

Now go to the Web and do the activity associated with this part of the chapter.

6.3 Understanding the impacts of unsustainable development: The Discovery Investigations

In 1911 the government formed a committee to make recommendations about a sustainable whaling industry to prevent a 'boom and bust'. After a delay caused by World War I, the committee came up with 36 recommendations and some of these are particularly interesting in the light of current environmental perspectives. Some of the key recommendations were:

> (2) The food for whales, whether consisting of plankton or fish, should be carefully investigated.
>
> (6) An experienced zoologist should be deputed to work for some time at one or more of the whaling stations.
>
> (11) The utmost economy must be observed in the utilization of all whale products, and every effort should be made to prevent the catching of more whales than can be commercially utilized.
>
> (22) Study of the life history and habits of the seals of the Dependencies [the name the British gave to the Antarctic] should form part of the work of the biologists attached to the proposed expedition.

(27) A complete hydrographical survey of the Dependencies is necessary both in the general interest of navigation and in the local interests of the whaling industry.

(35) Expenses incurred in connection with the economic development of the Dependencies and in particular with the preservation of the whaling industry may properly form charge against revenue raised in the Dependencies and additional taxation may rightly be imposed upon the whaling and sealing industries for the purpose of meeting such expenditure.

(Colonial Office, UK, 1920)

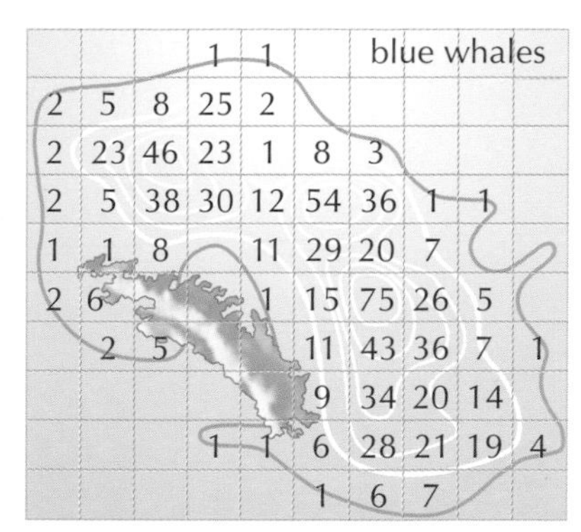

Figure 6.3 The distribution of blue whales caught at South Georgia in December 1926. The number in each box represents the number of animals caught. Contours are drawn at intervals of 10 animals.

Even from today's viewpoint, these are forward-thinking recommendations. However, the ideas behind this list are not so different from Weddell's views about protecting seal populations in 1825 — so again the 'green perspective' is neither new nor original. The committee must have realised that it could not stop whaling, but realised that understanding how to sustainably harvest the whales would allow the revenues to continue. You can get an idea of the sums involved if the costs are converted to current real terms (early 21st century). On this basis, the cost of the Discovery Investigations programme was almost £18.5 million up to 1932. From recommendation (35) it is evident that this was only a fraction of the revenue from South Georgia.

The Discovery Investigations began in 1925 and early results showed that the number of whales caught in just one month in 1926 from South Georgia was huge (Figure 6.3). A painting by Alister Hardy (a member of the Discovery Investigations team) conveys the industrial scale of the South Georgia whaling (Figure 6.4) in a more honest way than Figure 6.1. The investigations transformed our knowledge of whale biology as scientists were able to study recently caught carcasses. For example, they were able to measure the size and gestation period for different species, how often they conceived and so on. The investigations also gave the first demonstration of the importance of krill in the Antarctic marine ecosystem. However, there were notable omissions from the findings, the most obvious being a reliable estimate of whale numbers.

The investigations ended their fieldwork in the late 1940s although they continued to publish scientific work until the 1970s. Today, we can see that the hunters jumped species too quickly for the scientists to understand what was happening and the whaling industry collapsed through over-hunting. Without this understanding there was virtually no hope of regulating the system.

From one perspective you could argue that the investigations programme was a costly failure. However, it taught us a great deal about the Antarctic marine environment. It was the first to identify the continuous nature of the polar front around Antarctica; it discovered the life cycle of krill and linked their distribution to the distribution of whales (Figure 5.7); it also studied ocean circulation in these regions. What it could *not* do as a national scientific expedition, was to establish an international policy to prevent the whale slaughter.

Figure 6.4 A whale carcass awaiting flensing at Grytviken, by Alister Hardy.

At the end of World War II, it was estimated that there were around 50 000 blue whales in the Antarctic. By 1970, American scientists estimated that probably no more than 500 remained. One of the authors of this book has worked on research ships in the South Georgia region over a period of almost 10 years, and in this time has ~~seen~~ never seen a blue whale. Even with the benefits of modern technology, we cannot yet say with certainty where blue whales migrate to, what their full life history is, or even if they will ever recover to their former numbers — and this is despite their being the largest animals *ever* to have lived on Earth.

6.4 The International Whaling Commission

During the 'hunting frenzy' of the early 20th century, even some of the whalers felt that there should be some form of international management of the whaling industry and the League of Nations set up a Whaling Committee. By 1946 this had become the International Whaling Commission (IWC) and its terms of reference were given by a treaty known as the International Convention for the Regulation of Whaling. Its aims were similar to those of the Investigations but this time the organization was a real international agency. The treaty stated that the IWC should be responsible for 'the orderly development of the whaling industry', and initially the commission set quotas based on estimates of the stocks of whales. Unfortunately these quotas were based on pre-war population estimates, and in addition, despite setting a quota, the IWC did not assess the claims of individual nations to the whale stocks. Some countries (e.g. the USA) believed that 'freedom of the seas' was important, and that whaling could be managed by setting an overall catch quota. Factory ships would then sail wherever they wanted, report weekly catches, and when the quota was reached all whaling would be stopped.

- What was the flaw in this strategy?
- The whalers would have to be honest and not lie about numbers of whales caught.

All whaling countries continually and demonstrably lied about catches and of course whale numbers decreased. As a result the whaling nations found it increasingly difficult to make 'adequate' profits. In 1965 two eminent scientists wrote:

> The major Antarctic stocks of blue and fin whales could, if properly managed, produce annually, and in perpetuity, a total of 25 000 whales. However, they have been reduced far below the level which would provide these maximum sustainable yields and at present any catches in excess of about 4000 fin whales and a few blue whales would deplete the stocks. Despite this knowledge, in the 1964–65 season 14 000 fin whales were killed. ... Never was a case for international action so obvious, and perhaps the response been so inadequate.
>
> (Lucas and Cole, 1965)

Despite such strong language, it was not until 1982 that the IWC agreed to a moratorium on *all* whale stocks, to begin in 1985–86. This moratorium remains in force at the beginning of the 21st century. Although there were violent and global anti-whaling protests at this time, it was only commercial reasons that stopped whaling. There was simply not enough profit left. The IWC remains convinced that the populations of whales will recover now that hunting has ceased, and when this happens, according to the Convention, whaling should resume.

- Would you expect the whale numbers to recover to their pre-hunting levels?
- No. Different species have different rates of reproduction and will recover at different rates.

Minke whales (*Balaenoptera acutorostrata*) seem to be recovering very rapidly and at the start of the 21st century, the global population was estimated to be about 1 million animals. Other species have not recovered so well, and blue whale stocks do not appear to be recovering at all. However, if whaling resumed on a 'recovered' species then environmental groups would most likely find other reasons to protest against whaling. The politics of whaling are now governed less by scientific arguments about numbers of animals and reproduction rates, than by the ethics of killing whales.

- In view of the different rates of reproduction of whale species, how do you think a return to whaling should be managed?

- Different species should be declared 'available' to hunt *only* when they have exceeded their own targeted population levels. Further, there should be different quotas set for each individual species based on estimates of sustainable hunting. Of course, this depends on whalers being honest and not exceeding quotas.

The argument is complicated by the fact that, although commercial whaling ceased in 1985, 'scientific whaling' — that is whaling conducted for the purposes of studying the animals — has never stopped. The Japanese take approximately 400 minke whales per year and study the average age of the animals and reproductive rates. Using these data they can estimate animal numbers, and then work out how many whales could be sustainably harvested. The whale meat is also sold, but this contributes to the cost of the research.

6.4.1 The end of Antarctic whaling

As whales became commercially extinct, the whaling stations on South Georgia closed one by one. Eventually, even the largest and most efficient whaling station at Grytviken was closed in 1964. The whaling companies thought they would be able to resume whaling at a future date and so the stations were 'mothballed', with the companies leaving behind large amounts of the debris including whalebones, scrap metal, barrels, and even ships (Figure 6.5a–c, overleaf).

The arguments about whaling are complicated and a list of the current member countries of the IWC is an interesting example of modern environmental politics (Table 6.1, p.141).

- What do you notice about some of the countries in Table 6.1?

- Austria, Mongolia, San Marino and Switzerland are land-locked, with no direct access to the sea. In addition there are many small nations from the Caribbean.

Why would land-locked countries be members of an organization that controls whaling on the high seas? Some environmentalists have alleged that Japan is linking aid to less developed countries with undertakings to persuade them to vote with Japan at the IWC. To further complicate matters, even though you may have thought Iceland would be a member of the IWC, it withdrew citing disagreements with the scientific justification for the moratorium. It is now trying to rejoin the IWC, but still refuses to accept the moratorium. At the time of writing (2002) the balance on the

IWC between anti- and pro-whaling nations is very close, so jeopardizing the moratorium. This is a live issue because most scientists believe that minke whales could be sustainably harvested with a quota of several thousand animals a year. At the 2002 IWC meeting in Japan there was a vote on whether to allow Iceland back into the IWC and potentially swing the balance. However, the vote went against Iceland and so the moratorium currently stays in place.

(a)

(b)

(c)

Figure 6.5 (a) A whale vertebra lying on the beach at Husvik whaling station. (b) Debris at the Stromness whaling station on South Georgia. (c) Two catcher boats at Grytviken in South Georgia — when originally left they were floating, and have only sunk through vandalism.

Table 6.1 The member countries of the IWC in 2002 (IWC, 2002).

Antigua and Barbuda	Republic of Guinea	Panama
Argentina	India	Peru
Australia	Ireland	Portugal
Austria	Italy	Russian Federation
Benin	Japan	Saint Kitts and Nevis
Brazil	Kenya	Saint Lucia
Chile	Republic of Korea	Saint Vincent and The Grenadines
People's Republic of China	Mexico	San Marino
Costa Rica	Monaco	Senegal
Denmark	Mongolia	Solomon Islands
Dominica	Morocco	South Africa
Finland	Netherlands	Spain
France	New Zealand	Sweden
Gabon	Norway	Switzerland
Germany	Oman	UK
Grenada	Palau	USA

6.5 A modern land rush: territorial conflicts in Antarctica

The territorial claim staked in Antarctica by Britain in 1908 was followed by claims from New Zealand (1923), France (1924), Australia (1933), Norway (1939), Chile (1940) and finally Argentina (1942). Unfortunately, the Argentinian, Chilean and British territorial claims overlapped on the Antarctic Peninsula (Figure 6.6, overleaf). All these countries believed they had a valid claim. In the case of the Antarctic Peninsula, the British believed that they discovered it, and were actually administering part of it. The Chileans and Argentinians used the idea of geographical proximity. With such competing claims could you say which country, if any, owned the Antarctic Peninsula?

The Americans, who were present from almost the beginning of Antarctic exploration (Table 4.1), were watching events closely. By 1924 there was pressure from the American public who wanted to know why the USA had not made a territorial claim. Charles Hughes, the US Secretary of State said:

> It is the opinion of this department that the discovery of land unknown to civilisation even when coupled with formal taking possession does not support the valid claim of sovereignty unless the discovery is followed by an *actual settlement* [our italics] of the discovered country.
>
> (quoted in Sullivan, 1957)

Thus it became American policy not to recognize any country's Antarctic claims, but at the same time to reserve the right to make its own claim, and for its citizens to visit whenever they wanted. This policy is an extension of the 'high seas' argument that the Americans used to justify not allocating whale quotas to individual countries. The USA rapidly changed its tune in 1939 when Nazi Germany undertook an expedition to Antarctica and announced its intention to make a territorial claim. (The Germans were thwarted by the fact that their '*Neu-Schwabenland*' had already been claimed by the Norwegians!) The US Government responded by sending an expedition to the Antarctic. The Secretary of State specifically asked the members of the expedition to 'take appropriate steps such as dropping written claims from aeroplanes depositing such claims in cairns etc. which might persist in supporting a claim by the United States Government' (Sullivan, 1957). So much for non-recognition.

Nobody was really sure how to make territorial claims legally binding in an uninhabited region. One certainty was that a permanent human presence would help any territorial claim and sovereignty would be enhanced if, for example, a country could prove it was administering the region perhaps through operating a postal service. Britain had already set up and operated the first Antarctic post office on South Georgia in 1909.

In World War II, the conflict eventually reached Antarctica when the German ship *Pinguin* arrived in the Southern Ocean. The *Pinguin* had hidden guns and was disguised as a Greek cargo ship (painted in neutral colours) so that it could approach other shipping closely. In just 24 hours it captured three Norwegian factory ships and seven catcher boats off Queen Maud Land (see Figure 6.6). This was most of the

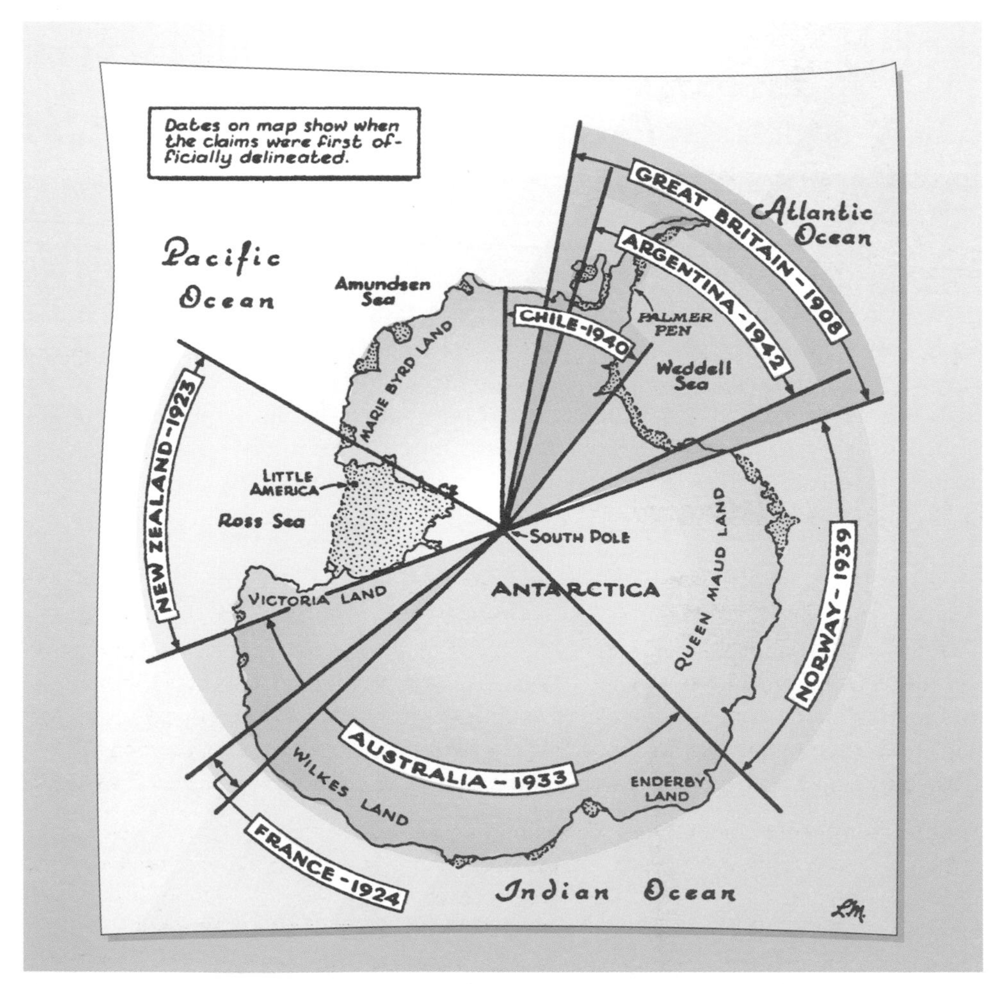

Figure 6.6 The locations and dates of territorial claims in Antarctica. This map was drawn in 1957 before the introduction of the Antarctic Treaty.

Norwegian whaling fleet and a valuable source of oil. To deny the use of the Antarctic Peninsula to the German raiders and to strengthen the British territorial claim, the British Admiralty sent a secret military expedition to the Antarctic in 1944 to establish a permanent presence. This was *Operation Tabarin* (named after a Paris nightclub — Figure 6.7a) and it established the first permanent base in Antarctica (Base A) at Port Lockroy, with eight men (Figure 6.7b). Around the same time, the Royal Navy laid mines around the Kerguelan Islands (the islands are French Territory and at about 69° E, they are a similar latitude to South Georgia), where the *Pinguin* had replenished food and supplies. At the time of writing (2002), the British Admiralty still consider these mines a danger to shipping.

(a)

(b)

Figure 6.7 (a) A poster for the nightclub Tabarin in Paris, which inspired the name of the British military expedition. (b) The British Base A, at Port Lockroy on the Antarctic Peninsula.

6.6 The post-war human invasion

After World War II, the British transferred operations to the civilian Falkland Islands Dependencies Survey (FIDS), which established more Antarctic bases (Figure 6.8, overleaf). At the same time, the US Navy was looking for new challenges and organized *Operation Highjump* (1946–47), the largest expedition ever to have gone to Antarctica. It is interesting to compare the British and American efforts. The British used two ships and placed generally less than 10 people at each base, but the American effort involved 13 warships, including an aircraft carrier, a submarine and almost 5000 men.

Not surprisingly the other interested nations were rather concerned at this development particularly as exploitable resources were being discovered at this time. *The New York Times* reported that *Highjump* had discovered uranium deposits, although this was denied by Admiral Richard Byrd, the expedition leader. Another US admiral stated that the objectives for *Highjump* included 'consolidating and extending United States sovereignty over the largest practicable area of the Antarctic continent'. But Byrd said the objectives were not diplomatic, scientific or economic; they were:

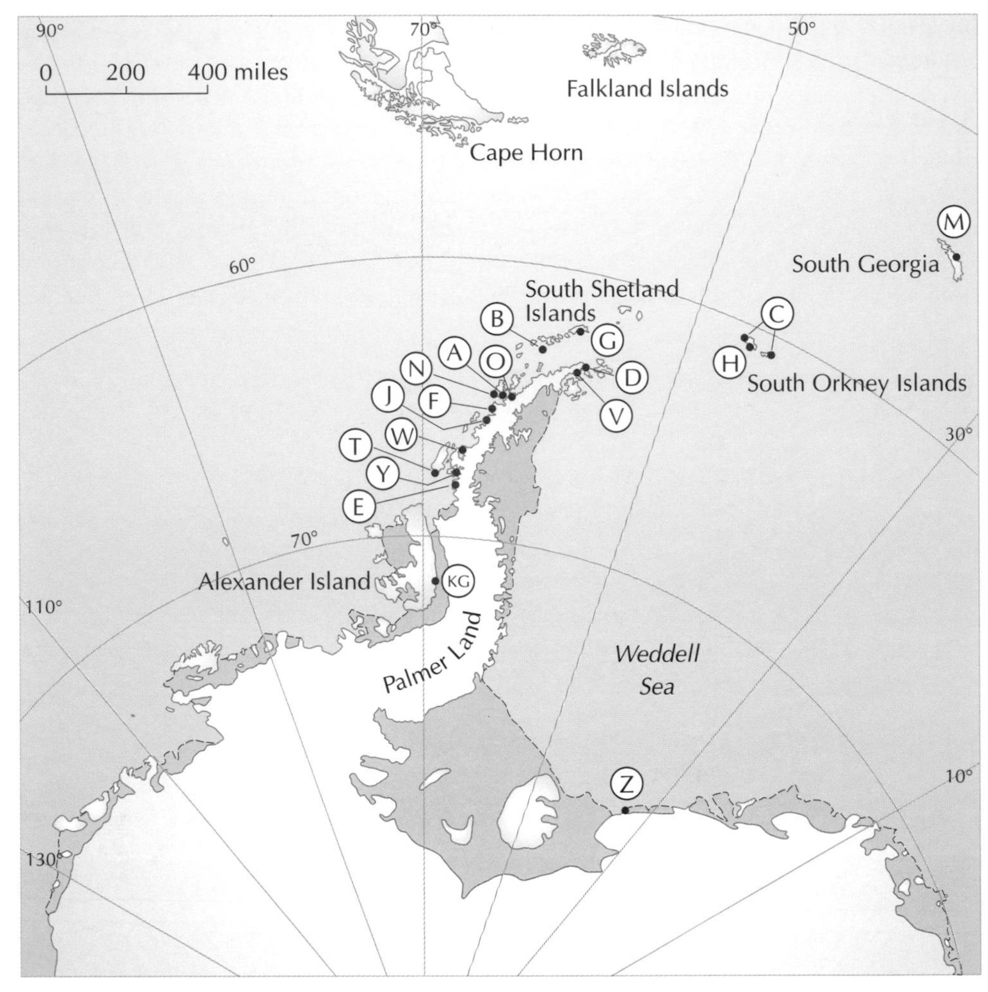

Figure 6.8 The locations of British bases (labelled by letter) in the British Antarctic Territory, established during and after World War II by *Operation Tabarin* and the Falkland Island Dependencies Survey. Each letter is the original identification label of the base; for example, 'A' points to the location of Base A at Port Lockroy.

> … primarily of a military nature, that is to train naval personnel and to test ships, planes and equipment under frigid zone conditions.
>
> (quoted in Sullivan, 1957)

And so the first military invasion of Antarctica occurred. Though *Highjump's* personnel were the first to visit the South Pole since Captain Scott, the main contribution of the operation was the acquisition of aerial photographs of the coast (Figure 6.9). The reality was that the military card had been played and the Americans claimed they had discovered up to 700 000 square miles of land.

6.7 Antarctic tempers rise

Following *Highjump* and *Tabarin*, the South American claimants were spurred into action. In one week in 1947, both Argentinian and Chilean ships sailed into Deception Island on the Antarctic Peninsula with the intention of setting up bases. One can only imagine what they thought when they found a British base already set up in the old whaling station. The situation was reaching a crisis point, with diplomatic notes being exchanged between London and Buenos Aires, and both countries sent warships south. In 1948, the Chileans upped the stakes with a visit by their President, the first Head of State to visit Antarctica. He said:

> The bad habits of antiquated European imperialism is threatening with arms and violence to seize these lands of ours from Chile and America.
>
> (President Gabriel Gonzalez Videla, 1948, quoted in Sullivan, 1957)

The Chileans and Argentinians then issued a joint declaration, saying that their rights to Antarctica were 'unquestionable'. With the start of the Cold War and eyes elsewhere, the Americans suggested 'some form of internationalization', but this was unacceptable to many parties. Numerous small incidents, some involving gunfire, continued, and in 1953 the British actually deported two Argentinians from Deception via the Falkland Islands. By this time something really had to be done. The only available option was the International Court of Justice in The Hague. In May 1955 the British applied for arbitration and told the court that the continent was first discovered by Edward Bransfield on the 30th of January 1820, and that a British magistrate had been stationed at Deception

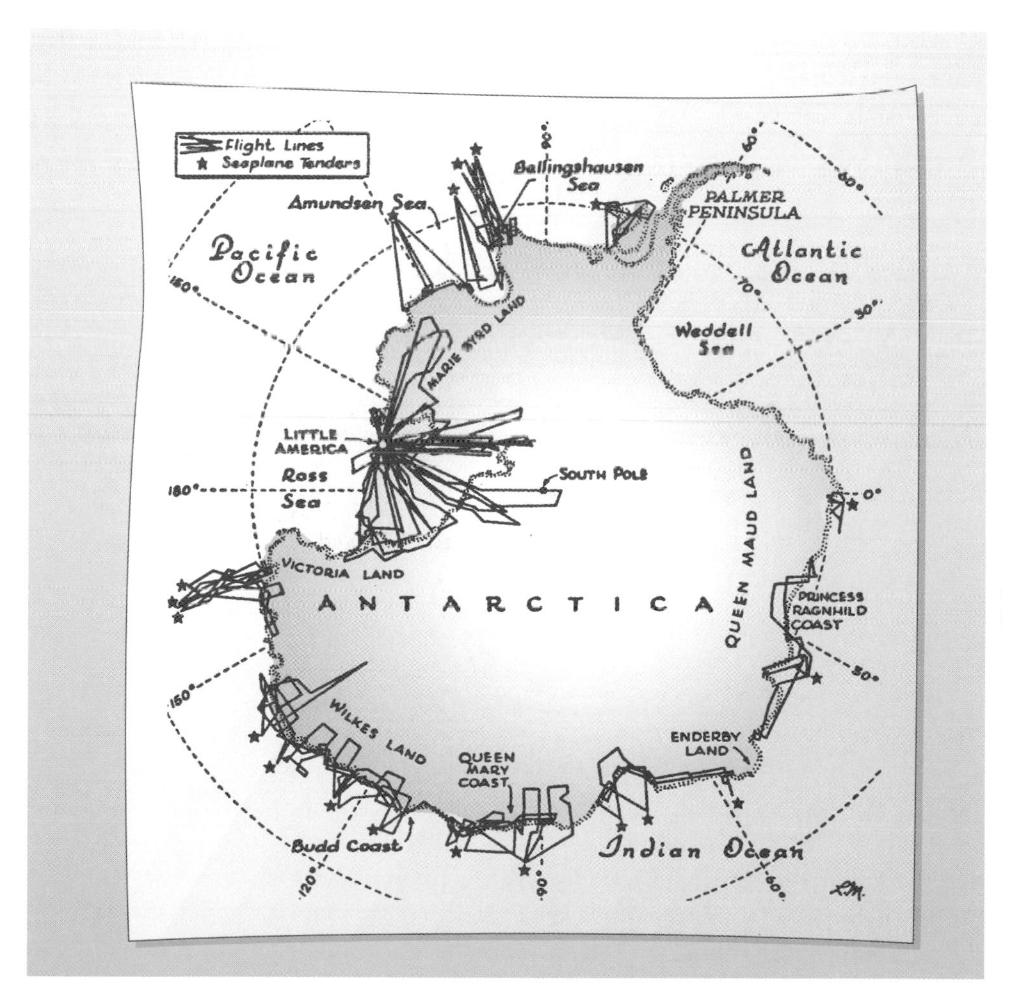

Figure 6.9 The extensive photographic surveying flights undertaken during *Operation Highjump*.

Island during every whaling season from 1910 to 1930 — long before any other government had laid claim to the area. The Chileans and Argentinians countered this by simply refusing to recognize the power of the court! The only real solution to avoid conflict lay in the proposal of the US to 'internationalize' Antarctica.

6.8 Peace breaks out: The International Geophysical Year of 1957–58

While the territorial disputes continued, Antarctica was becoming a continent for scientific study. There had already been two scientific events called 'International Polar Years' mainly concentrating on the Arctic — the first in 1882–83, and the second in 1932–33. The American Lloyd Berkner proposed a new global scientific expedition to study the Earth at the peak of the eleven-year cycle of sunspot activity. This proposal led to the International Geophysical Year (IGY, 1957–58), whose logo is shown in Figure 6.10. It was the first international scientific programme and 67 countries were involved. Antarctic science is important since it is the perfect natural laboratory for studying, amongst other things, the aurora, cosmic rays, geomagnetism and, of course, glaciology. Although many nations had been working in Antarctica previously, there was no global perspective. For example, there was no network of weather stations and so no understanding of how the weather actually behaved around Antarctica. The massive increase in scientific effort during IGY made this network possible when 12 nations agreed to maintain year-round scientific stations.

Figure 6.10 The logo of the International Geophysical Year 1957–58. The angle of the South Pole towards us indicates the importance of Antarctica.

The Antarctic component of the IGY was coordinated by the Special Committee for Antarctic Research (SCAR — later the 'Special' was changed to 'Scientific'). SCAR helped to establish 44 Antarctic and sub-Antarctic research stations and chose the location of some key sites. These were the Antarctic Peninsula, the geographic South Pole (the US set up the Amundsen–Scott Station), the Pole of Inaccessibility (the Soviet Sovetskaya Station) and the South Geomagnetic Pole (the Soviet Vostok Station). Simultaneously, the British Commonwealth Trans-Antarctic Expedition, led by Vivian Fuchs and Everest conqueror Edmund Hillary, made a successful cross-Antarctic traverse, using both dogs and mechanized transport, that provided the first measurements of ice thickness all the way across the continent. The impact of the IGY on Antarctica was seen not only in the vast expansion in scientific output from the continent, but also in the proliferation of Antarctic bases (Figure 6.11).

- Look at Figure 6.11. How did the distribution of Antarctic research stations change during the IGY?

- More research stations were established, especially in the centre of the continent away from the coasts.

On the international stage at this time, the Cold War was in full swing with global peace threatened by the nuclear strategy of a mutually assured destruction, the Vietnam war, the erection of the Berlin Wall, the Suez Crisis and so on. However, in Antarctica there was cooperation — but no real solution. The situation at the end of the IGY was summed up perfectly by the journalist Walter Sullivan:

> Thus the situation stands today. There are postmasters with no mail to handle, Royal magistrates with no cases to try, brass plaques that look out over

windswept mountains where men have visited but once. The flags, claim sheets, and other emblems dropped from the planes of various nations lie congealed into the crust over the continent. To those who have seen the vastness of the Antarctic ice sheet, the stark splendour of its mountains, incredible fury of its winds, these displays of national rivalry around its fringes seem strangely absurd.

(Sullivan, 1957)

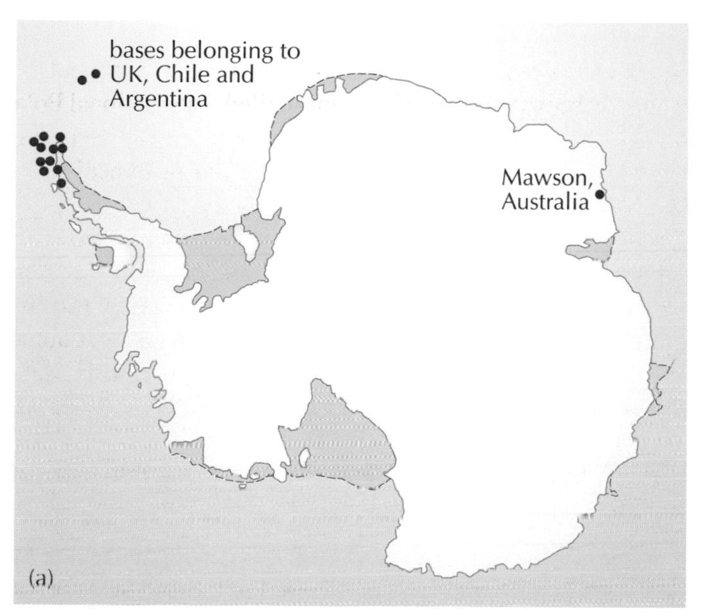

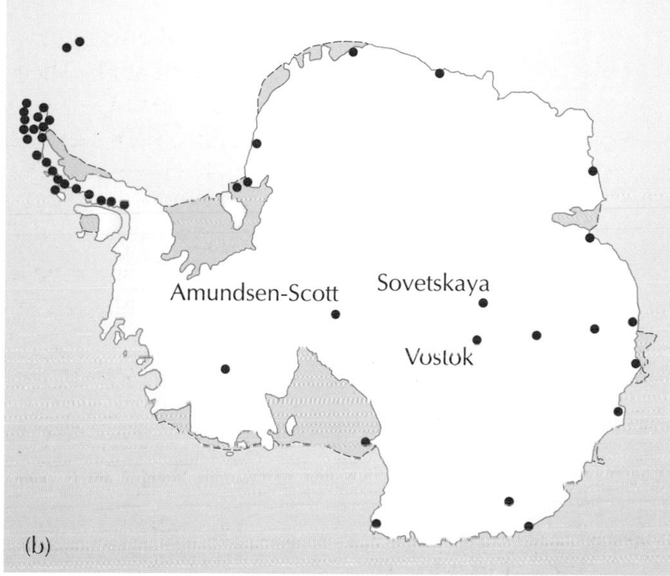

Figure 6.11 The expansion in the number of Antarctic research stations during the IGY. (a) The locations of Antarctic research stations before the IGY. (b) The locations of Antarctic research stations during the IGY. Amundsen–Scott base is at the South Pole, Vostok at the South Geomagnetic Pole and Sovetskaya at the Pole of Inaccessibility.

6.9 The Antarctic Treaty

If the scientific results from the IGY were important, then the political outcome was momentous. Many countries that had never previously worked in Antarctica had established permanent bases and the US suggested an international agreement be negotiated between the 12 nations who established year-round bases. These twelve nations met secretly in Washington every two weeks from the middle of 1958 until early 1959 to develop a solution. They produced the **Antarctic Treaty**, signed on 1 December 1959, which came into effect on 23 June 1961. The Treaty itself is rather short — it only consists of 14 articles. Some of these were deliberately imprecise and so open to problems with interpretation.

Perhaps the key article in the Antarctic Treaty is Article IV (see Box 6.1, overleaf). What this says in an ambiguous way, is that disputes of territorial sovereignty are insoluble and so should be put aside. Various authors have interpreted it as being either a step towards co-ownership of Antarctica, or renunciation. The reality is that it puts *all* sovereignty claims into abeyance until a later and unspecified date. The Treaty itself has no expiry date and so will remain in force indefinitely; it also states that new decisions about international regulation south of 60° S must be made by 'unanimous agreement', that is, by consensus. But is a treaty having only 12 signatories a fair and practical way to determine the fate of a huge global resource?

Article IX of the Treaty allows other countries to become so-called Consultative Parties (CPs), if they engage in '*substantial scientific research activity*' — but what does substantial mean? Any country that signs the Treaty at this level can vote on future agreements. In addition, a second, lower level of membership was instigated for nations who, whilst not engaged in substantial research, agree to abide by the principles of the Treaty (called Non-Consultative Parties, NCPs). In August 2002 there were 27 CPs, and a further 17 NCPs.

Box 6.1 Article IV of the Antarctic Treaty

1 Nothing contained in the present Treaty shall be interpreted as:
(a) a renunciation by any Contracting Party of previously asserted rights of or claims to territorial sovereignty in Antarctica;
(b) a renunciation or diminution by any Contracting Party of any basis of claim to territorial sovereignty in Antarctica which it may have whether as a result of its activities or those of its nationals in Antarctica, or otherwise;
(c) prejudicing the position of any Contracting Party as regards its recognition or non-recognition of any other State's rights of, or claim, or basis of claim to territorial sovereignty in Antarctica.

2 No acts or activities taking place while the present Treaty is in force shall constitute a basis for asserting, supporting or denying a claim to territorial sovereignty in Antarctica or create any rights of sovereignty in Antarctica. No new claim, or enlargement of an existing claim, to territorial sovereignty in Antarctica shall be asserted while the present Treaty is in force.

Consensus decisions can take a long time to reach. Furthermore, all countries have the same voting rights as each other whatever their budget for Antarctic research — the United States has a budget of about £200 million per year whereas New Zealand has a budget of about £2 million per year — each country has one vote. We can assume that some nations have more influence than others in what is now called the **Antarctic Treaty System** (ATS), but consensus can break down and an individual country can decide an issue.

Because countries can become a CP by setting up a year-round Antarctic research station there has been a proliferation of bases on the tip of the Antarctic Peninsula, for example on King George Island (Figure 6.12). This island is easily accessible to non-icebreaking ships (Bransfield found it in a wooden sailing ship) and building a base here does not require sophisticated technology. In the words of the Polish Academy of Sciences it is now 'somewhat overcrowded', with nine stations present over the winter of 2000 (some right next to each other), and in summer the number rises to at least 10, though usually more. Four of the countries here do not work elsewhere in the Antarctic and the obvious question is are they doing the same 'research' as other King George Island stations?

Despite these problems, overall the Treaty has been a success and there has been no Antarctic military conflict. The Treaty has also led the way in international environmental law with the adopting of a further four agreements (Table 6.2).

Table 6.2 International agreements adopted under the Antarctic Treaty System.

Agreement	Year
Agreed Measures for the Conservation of Antarctic Fauna and Flora	1964
Convention for the Conservation of Antarctic Seals (CCAS)	1972
Convention for the Conservation of Antarctic Marine Living Resources (CCAMLR)	1982
Protocol on Environmental Protection to the Antarctic Treaty	1998

Each of the agreements in Table 6.2 was a major step forward in the governance of Antarctica. The Agreed Measures covered one of the most important environmental issues by banning the importation of non-indigenous species. It also stated that animals could not be killed without a permit, and allowed for the designation of specially protected areas. Today, this agreement has been superseded by the Environmental Protocol (1998). Like the Antarctic Treaty, CCAS applies south of 60° S and its purpose was to protect seals if sealing was to recommence, and to completely prohibit the killing of Ross and Antarctic fur seals. CCAMLR is very different and its boundary is not 60° S, but the polar front — much further north than the other agreements. It controls Antarctic fisheries using what is called an ecosystem approach rather than a straight quota system. We'll go into this in more detail in the following section. The Protocol on Environmental Protection has an interesting history. It arose from the demise of another convention which, despite being reached by consensus, was publicly and painfully put to the sword.

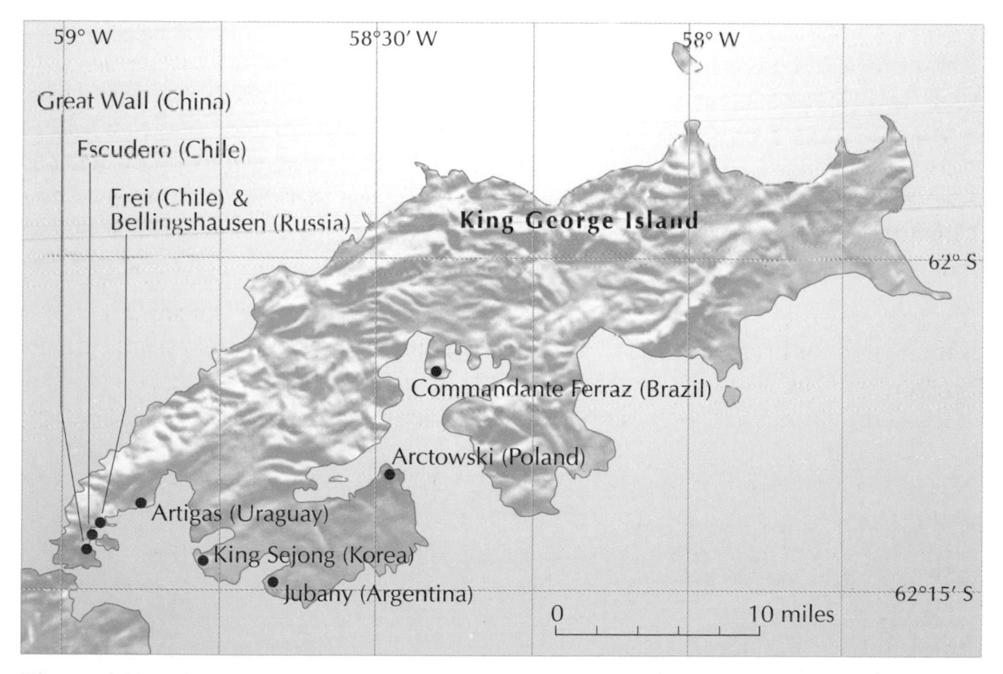

Figure 6.12 Winter stations on King George Island on the Antarctic Peninsula in 2000. Could we expect meteorological data collected at Great Wall station to be very different from that collected at Frei?

6.10 The failure of the Convention on the Regulation of Antarctic Mineral Resource Activities (CRAMRA)

The Antarctic Treaty does not mention mineral resources. This omission is surprising since the earliest explorers found coal, and regions of Antarctica are geologically very similar to the mineral rich areas of South America, South Africa and Australia (Figure 4.14a). However, regulation of potential mining activity did not occur until 1970 when Britain and New Zealand first raised the issue after being approached by oil companies. The Treaty nations agreed a mining moratorium until a comprehensive agreement could be reached, and by 1988 the Convention on the Regulation of Antarctic Mineral Resource Activities (CRAMRA) was on the table. As this agreement had been reached by consensus, it should have been a formality for the nations to sign and ratify it. Exploration and mining were to be allowed, but with strict controls. Before any major activity the environmental impact would be reviewed, and no activity would be allowed unless all the Treaty nations agreed that there would be no risk to the environment. Unfortunately the clause that stopped mining would only come into play if there were 'significant' adverse environmental effects. Many environmental groups were fundamentally opposed to mining and they launched a major international campaign to stop CRAMRA being ratified.

6.10.1 Greenpeace goes to Antarctica

The world had not stood still since the Treaty had been agreed and environmental groups were making their presence felt in Antarctic affairs. The environmental group Greenpeace had been on the global scene for a couple of decades and had a reputation for high impact environmental protests, for example against whaling and the testing of nuclear weapons. As the organization (and of course its funding) grew, it campaigned on wider issues, and what could be bigger than violation of the 'last wilderness'? Greenpeace could have just publicized the issue of Antarctica, but it was much bolder and decided to send its own expedition to the region and in 1987 built an Antarctic base (Figure 6.13).

Although this expedition was certainly not the first private one to visit Antarctica, Greenpeace was the first environmental non-governmental organization (NGO) to do so, and ultimately its aim was to have Antarctica declared an international 'World Park'. It even tried to become a Treaty CP by conducting scientific research at its base, and onboard its ship. However, Article XIII of the ATS makes it clear that Treaty CP

Figure 6.13 World Park Base set up by Greenpeace in 1987 on Ross Island.

membership is only open to 'any state which is a Member of the United Nations' — and of course an NGO is not a state.

The Greenpeace principles for the 'World Park' were simple:

> 1 The wilderness values of Antarctica should be protected;
>
> 2 There should be complete protection for Antarctic wildlife (though limited fishing would be permissible);
>
> 3 Antarctica should remain a zone of limited scientific activity with cooperation and coordination between scientists of all nations;
>
> 4 Antarctica should remain a zone of peace, free of all weapons.
>
> (May, 1988)

At first sight the principles seem sensible, but look again at the language. Greenpeace had previously criticised the vague and ambiguous terms in the ATS — which it still publicly supported — but it had made the same mistake itself. What exactly are 'wilderness values'? Despite these problems the campaign was a great success and Greenpeace brilliantly exploited the public perception of Antarctica. As well as building an environmentally friendly base it visited and inspected existing research stations and was shocked by what it saw. Greenpeace's publicity machine highlighted violations of the Antarctic Treaty with photographic evidence of rubbish dumps full of non-biodegradable waste such as plastics, metals and even trucks. It also filmed some spectacular footage of the French actually blowing up penguins while building a runway at Dumont d'Urville (66° S 140° E). By suggesting that previous agreements (even ones they publicly thought enforced good standards) were not good enough, how could people trust CRAMRA?

As mentioned above, the publicity was highly successful and not just in influencing public opinion. In 1981 there were 25 signatories to the Treaty, but by 1988, when CRAMRA was ready to be signed, numbers had risen to 38. At the same time, countries that were not part of the ATS (e.g. Malaysia) were arguing in the UN that Antarctica was 'the common heritage of mankind'. How could 38 nations decide its fate? In 1989, the Argentinian ship *Bahia Paraiso* was wrecked on the Antarctic Peninsula. This event demonstrated the vulnerability of the region to oil pollution and thus increased the pressure on all nations in Antarctica.

CRAMRA was built on consensus by the Treaty nations — they only had to sign and ratify it. But, by now public opinion was against CRAMRA. The first country to refuse was Australia, followed by France. However, it was New Zealand that finally finished off CRAMRA; they had actually already signed but refused to ratify the treaty. The need for 'unanimous agreement' torpedoed CRAMRA and brought about crisis in the Antarctic Treaty System. Consensus had been broken and the ensuing vigorous public debate led to the UK and Chile calling for a special Treaty meeting to discuss comprehensive measures to protect the Antarctic environment. The ATS nations responded by agreeing the Protocol on Environmental Protection in 1991, with most parties signing immediately. However, it took until 1998 to come into force.

In an ironic twist, many of the pioneering environmental controls in CRAMRA were simply transferred to the protocol. The latter is a very tough international agreement and it has had a tremendous effect. Antarctica was designated a 'natural reserve devoted to science' with various consequences. On the question of mining, the protocol bans all 'mineral resource activity' except bonafide scientific research. It banished huskies from the region by 1994 as they were non-indigenous. All rubbish in certain categories now has to be removed, and discharge of waste materials into the sea is not allowed. There has also been a very large and expensive clean-up of abandoned bases.

An **Environmental Impact Assessment** (EIA) is now required for *any* activity in Antarctica, and activities can only proceed if there is sufficient information to determine that their impact is acceptable. Essentially this EIA requirement is the effective gatekeeper of Antarctica. Any activity that has an impact considered more than minor must undergo a **Comprehensive Environmental Evaluation** (CEE), which is then reviewed under the ATS system.

One could argue that the rejection of CRAMRA — an agreement that would have allowed mineral exploitation — has created a much tougher system that affects *all* Antarctic activities from tourism to science. However, the mining issue is not permanently buried as it has only been prohibited for 50 years. It is most likely that discussion will recommence by about 2035.

6.11 Antarctica today

Antarctica is now well governed and has some of the toughest environmental regulations in the world. Although science remains the dominant activity, for this final stage of our Antarctic journey we will examine how the agreements of the ATS control current activities.

6.11.1 CCAMLR and ecosystem management

A traditional fishery, such as those in the North Atlantic, is regulated by what is called the single-species approach. This system bases catch quotas upon estimates of the abundance of individual species. However, there have been many cases where single-species fisheries have collapsed despite the quota system, from the Antarctic whales, to the Canadian cod fishery and North Sea herring. The approach has two basic flaws (assuming everyone involved is honest). The first is that governments tend to set targets rather than strict limits — after all it would be a shame to throw back what you have already caught if you had brought up too much. A more serious deficiency is that the system does not take into account any interaction between species.

- Recall the example in Chapter 3 (Section 3.2) where interactions between fish species are the suspected cause of an over-fished resource failing to recover. What was the resource and what kind of ecological interaction was involved?

- The resource was Atlantic cod in Newfoundland. Recovery is possibly inhibited by an increase in smaller predatory fish that eat cod fry (See Box 3.1).

In contrast, CCAMLR (Table 6.2) controls the exploitation of the Antarctic marine environment using an ecosystem approach that is based on the relationship between all the different components in the ecosystem. It starts by defining the northern boundaries of the Antarctic ecosystem as the polar front, which is much further north than the traditional 60° S latitude and includes South Georgia and Kerguelan, and the whole ecosystem within this area is relevant. If, for example, you were setting a catch limit on krill, you would have to base this value on an understanding of *all* the ways that the different organisms in the ecosystem rely on it. You can see that this would be a complicated process because krill is a keystone species with many dependent predators (Chapter 5). We must also understand how changing the environment could affect krill numbers *before* setting a Total Allowable Catch (TAC) based upon the 'precautionary principle'. According to this principle, the fishery must be sustainable with the effects of dependent species (e.g. penguins and seals in the case of krill) being understood before a fishery can begin. CCAMLR have set a TAC for krill using this approach, but the current catch is only approximately 1% of this value with 98 400 tonnes being fished in 2001. The ecosystem approach is progressive (even Greenpeace supports it), and within the next 30 years the remainder of the North Atlantic fisheries may be governed in the same way. We use 'may' because the nations that fish in the North Atlantic do not have the foundation of the ATS to build on and so it will be a difficult or perhaps impossible political process.

The CCAMLR ecosystem approach should lead us to expect some species to increase in numbers when their predators, or their competitors for food, are harvested.

- Which other Antarctic animals could have exploited any 'extra' food made available by the drastic reduction in whale numbers?

- Penguins, albatross and seals (Chapter 5).

We noted earlier that in 1958 there were fewer than 100 pairs of fur seals left on South Georgia. However, since hunting of seals stopped the seal population increase has been staggering, and by the end of the 20th century there were probably over 1 million fur seals on the island. This extraordinary recovery has been attributed to a combination of the protection of the seals by the CCAS, but probably more importantly to the extra availability of food caused by the reduction in whale numbers. Although the cause is uncertain the effect is clear: on South Georgia and other sub-Antarctic islands seals are expanding into areas once inhabited by other animals such as penguins, and are possibly driving them away through competition. The ecosystem is rapidly changing, and there are now some seal experts who believe that the only way to prevent numbers increasing even further would be to amend the CCAS to allow fur seals to be culled. But could you see that being allowed?

Another problem with the CCAMLR approach is highlighted by the wealth of unprotected resources. In most parts of the world, fisheries protection is a common naval role but in the CCAMLR region there are few such ships, and the 60° S line presents a problem because of the non-military requirement. Fish species such as the Patagonian toothfish (*Dissostichus eleginoides*) and the Antarctic toothfish (*Dissostichus mawsoni*) are today's 'goldmines', and the campaign against pirate fishing is very active. One recent Greenpeace press release was entitled '*Business as usual for CCAMLR as Antarctica's fish and wildlife hang in the balance*'. If you think this is overstated you can visit the CCAMLR website and download its reports. The scale of the problem is clear; for example, its 2001 report stated:

> Paragraph 5.4 The Chair of the Scientific Committee advised the Commission that the catches reported from [an area outside the CCAMLR region] were not credible. Therefore the Committee 'concluded that practically all the toothfish catches reported from [this area] represent catches taken as a result of … fishing … inside the Convention Area'.

(CCAMLR Report, 2001)

However CCAMLR regulations call for a TAC to be set based on what is *reported* to have been caught within the Convention area, even though this may be a serious underestimate of the actual catch.

- What would be the effect of setting a TAC based on actual catches rather than reported catches?

- The TAC would be much lower.

Even legal toothfish fishing causes problems because the fish are caught using longline hooks rather than nets. The ships trail thousands of baited hooks on lines many kilometres long. Unfortunately, seabirds dive to take the bait as the hooks are deployed, become trapped and are dragged underwater and drowned. The problems of longlining are not limited to the CCAMLR region because this method is used all over the world. However, for species such as albatross, which like blue whales are long-lived and slow to reproduce, the attrition rate has been staggering. A recent census showed a drop of 76 000 albatross in just a five-year period in the Falkland Islands. The same pattern seems to be appearing in South Georgia and Kerguelan. CCAMLR has taken a series of measures to reduce this problem of bird bycatch, but a global solution is required if seabirds such as the albatross are to be saved.

6.11.2 Research

Science in Antarctica has continued to develop and expand. Many nations conduct large year-round research programmes, and over the years Antarctic science has contributed much to our understanding of how the Earth works. At the beginning of the 21st century, this research is contributing to an understanding of how other planets may work; for example, the endolithic communities in the Dry Valleys (Figure 5.5) are thought to represent possible life forms that may be found on Mars. The most famous Antarctic scientific advance to date is considered to be the discovery of the **ozone hole** (Box 6.2) by the British Antarctic Survey in 1985.

Box 6.2 The Antarctic ozone hole

Ozone (O_3) is a gas that is both created and destroyed by natural processes. It exists at low levels in the atmosphere, and the stratosphere ozone molecules protect life on Earth by absorbing ultra-violet light that can cause damage to living cells. Unfortunately, in the second half of the 20th century, the introduction of synthetic chemical compounds such as chlorofluorocarbons (CFCs) (once used in refrigerators and aerosols) and halons (in fire extinguishers) upset the natural balance. The compounds break up the ozone through complex chemical reactions and remove it from the atmosphere. This process, when combined with the very cold winter atmospheric conditions around Antarctica, creates a situation where ozone is destroyed very rapidly. Although we began using these CFCs and halons at the end of World War II, it was not until 1985 that scientists at the British Antarctic Survey demonstrated the presence of a region of very low ozone concentration over Antarctica at the end of the Antarctic winter. This 'hole' has been observed every year since, and it has become progressively larger (Figure 6.14).

Scientific proof that the ozone depletion was derived from human activity was the first conclusive evidence of our negative impact on the whole planet.

The international community rapidly responded and quickly adopted what became known as the Montreal Protocol to protect the ozone layer. The manufacture of CFCs and halons has been banned, but unfortunately these chemicals last for decades in the atmosphere so it will take at least another 50 years for the ozone levels to recover.

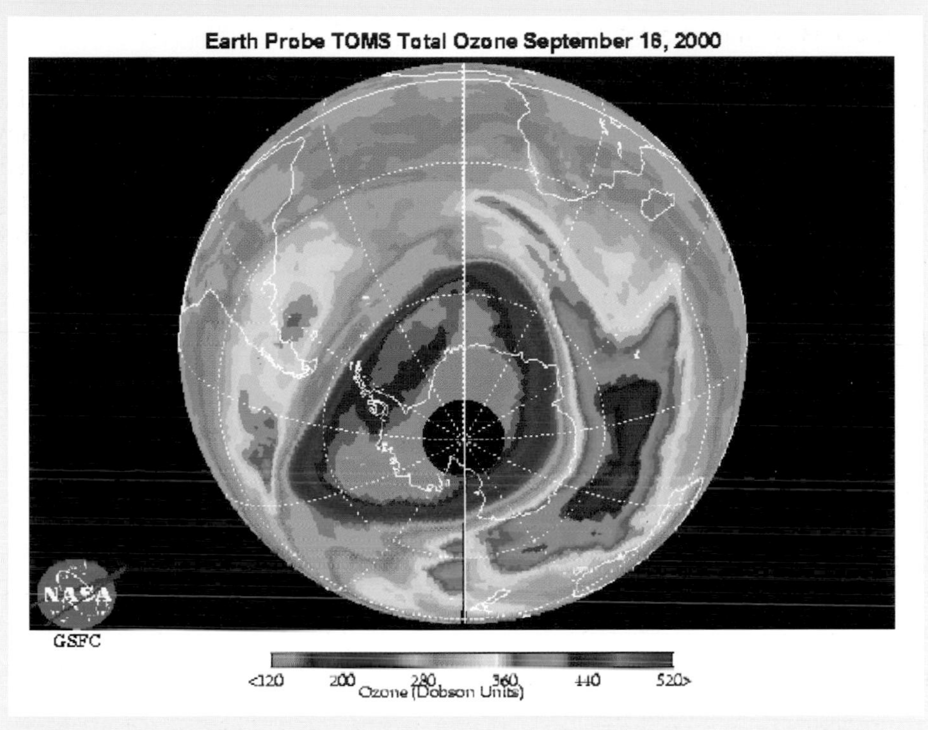

Figure 6.14 A satellite map of the ozone hole over Antarctica in September 2000 from data collected with the Total Ozone Mapping Spectrometer (TOMS).

More recently perhaps, the most exciting event has been the discovery of vast freshwater lakes deep beneath the Antarctic ice cap. The largest of these lakes is buried 3.75 km beneath the Russian Vostok Station and it was mapped in 1996 by Martin Siegert, a British scientist. It became known as Lake Vostok and is approximately 240 km × 50 km and up to 1000 m deep. This lake may be hundreds of thousands, or even millions of years old, and it was formed because the ice is so heavy that in some places at the bottom of the sheet it melts because of the huge pressure on it from above. Scientists believe that the lake water has been out of contact with the atmosphere for over 500 000 years and could therefore contain unique microbes and life-forms. Vostok also has another focus for research however. In the 1980s work began to drill a deep core of ice to study trapped gases to help reconstruct the past climate of the Earth. You will encounter the results of this research in Book 3.

- Would the climate scientists have had to prepare an EIA?
- No, they started their work before the Protocol came into force in 1998.

Siegert's work on Lake Vostok had an immediate impact. NASA became interested in testing the technology used to sample the lake because conditions could be similar to those found on Europa, an ice-covered moon of Jupiter. But the lake is pristine, and with no EIA the climate scientists were drilling towards it using a mixture of kerosene and anti-freeze to lubricate the drill. Penetration of the lake would certainly create an environmental impact that would be greater than 'minor or transitory'. According to the Protocol there should be a CEE for the ATS to review, and in 1998 drilling was stopped at a depth of 3623 m — within 150 m of the lake. The Russians submitted a draft CEE to the ATS in 2002 proposing further drilling, but it is controversial and drilling is unlikely to go ahead at present. It is likely that drilling will eventually take place, but new methods will have to be developed to avoid pollution of Lake Vostok.

6.11.3 Antarctic tourism

Antarctica has been a fast-growing tourist destination since the late 1950s when both Argentina and Chile took a few hundred fare-paying passengers to the South Shetland Islands using naval ships.

- Why would these countries take tourists to Antarctica?
- It was an attempt to demonstrate sovereignty.

The tourist industry developed a style called 'expedition cruising', whereby tour companies took cruise ships south and employed scientists to educate the passengers about Antarctica. It seemed to work and tourist numbers steadily increased. By the 1980s there were about 1000 people visiting the area each year, even as the CRAMRA negotiations were continuing. When tourists visited research stations they were as horrified as Greenpeace at what they saw and naturally voiced their protests loudly (Figure 6.15).

Some nations prevented tourists from visiting their bases altogether, but this was difficult to achieve as the Treaty provides freedom of access and many bases were already abandoned. Tourist numbers continued to rise, and as the industry developed, the tour operators formed their own Antarctic NGO in 1991 — the International Association of

Figure 6.15 Tourists walk past debris left by a national Antarctic programme.

Antarctica Tour Operators (IAATO) — with the aim of responsible private sector travel in Antarctica. IATTO now has 46 members and attends Treaty meetings as expert observers.

The Protocol on Environmental Protection requires that abandoned bases and waste dumps in Antarctica must be 'cleared-up'. For example, the British Antarctic Survey (BAS) and the UK Antarctic Heritage Trust (a charity) carried out a spectacular job of restoring Port Lockroy (Base A, Figure 6.7b). By converting a derelict station into a museum they have created one of the most popular visitor sites in Antarctica.

The impact of tourism is now on the agenda; for example, the vandalism seen in Figures 6.5b and Figure 6.16. But more importantly, what about other effects such as the visiting of penguin colonies by tourists? Most cruise ships only visit the northern end of the Antarctic Peninsula on short ten-day trips. This means that they repeatedly visit the same sites (the data are collected by IAATO and presented at ATS meetings). Port Lockroy (Figure 6.7b) has been in the top five most visited sites since data collection started, and in 2001–02, almost 6400 people landed there. The BAS conducted a study which showed that tourism was having no effect on the penguins here when compared with undisturbed regions nearby. Similar work has concluded that the effects of tourists are negligible when compared with long-term natural environmental changes. These results are not surprising as IAATO provides its passengers with comprehensive guidelines on responsible behaviour that have been agreed by the Antarctic Treaty nations. These guidelines are combined with a high staff/passenger ratio on landings, which ensures proper control. Self-regulation appears to have worked so far, and any adverse effects of Antarctic tourism seem to have been minimal.

Figure 6.16 Typical graffiti found at a whaling station on South Georgia. This would suggest that not all incidents of vandalism are a result of tourism.

- Why do you think self-regulation appears to be working?
- The tourists are visiting a region where they *believe* they have to act in a responsible manner and are strictly controlled by the tour operators.

In the early years of the 21st century, a traveller has many choices connected with Antarctic tourism. You could go on a cruise ship, a small yacht or even fly to the

South Pole. IAATO has estimated that by 2005 there will be up to 22 ships operating in the Antarctic, not counting private yachts. This number could mean up to 20 000 people visiting the area each year (Figure 6.17). If self-regulation continues to work there should not be a problem. Of course, the situation could rapidly change if a large cruise ship was wrecked — something that is perhaps not so unlikely as the Southern Ocean is generally poorly surveyed. Any resulting pollution or loss of life could certainly change public opinion.

(a) (b) (c) (d)

Figure 6.17 Modern ship-based Antarctic tourism. (a) The restored Antarctic research station Port Lockroy flying a national flag and now operating as a museum. Beautiful scenery and weather, some tourists interacting with the animals by taking photographs, and others returning to the ship with bags of shopping. (b) The radio room in Port Lockroy. (c) A lecturer (with yellow radio) telling tourists about a historic food cache. (d) Tourists learning about whaling.

6.12 Conclusions of Chapter 6

The Antarctic continent was discovered less than 200 years ago, with the first huts being built much more recently. We started this chapter with the depressing story of the slaughter of the great whales and the potential military conflict over territorial claims. Since then, however, the story has been generally positive. Given a remote and special region, little historical baggage and a pressing need for conservation, nations have developed the ATS — a system based on consensus. Now in theory even the 'little guy' can have a say on Antarctic issues. But is this really the case? A look at the membership of the ATS shows that there are only two CPs from the less developed world that are not from South America (China and India), and no African members apart from South Africa. We also have to ask whether the Treaty needs to be updated? For example, is the 60° S latitude a sensible limit for the Antarctic Treaty area? Figure 5.1 showed that the polar waters extend much further north. CCAMLR recognized this 20 years after the Treaty was signed and defined a much larger region. Would a more northerly limit have made any difference?

It certainly could have made a difference in terms of military action. During the Falklands War, Argentina invaded South Georgia, and in this particular battle several Argentinians lost their lives, with one British injury. An undefended BAS base was also captured. However, south of 60° S, both countries were still working together. Within 22 days South Georgia was recaptured. The British were aware that Argentina had built a base on Thule (59.5° S, 27.4° W, the most southerly of the South Sandwich Islands) and they set out to take control. British troops removed what diplomats had described as the 'illegal occupation' in June of 1982, to much Argentinian protest at the UN. The British then returned in February 1983 to blow up the Argentine base. We cannot predict what could have happened if the ATS limit was similar to the CCAMLR one, but there was no military action — and cooperation continued — south of the treaty boundary.

In terms of resource management, CCAMLR was the first international fisheries treaty to use an ecosystem approach for sustainable development. It is a model for other areas and, but for illegal fishing, would be even more successful.

With the introduction of the Environmental Protocol and the rise of tourism, activities in Antarctica have completely changed. You may have felt tourism should not have been allowed because of potential environmental impacts, but could you say its impact would be greater than that of the nine research stations on King George Island?

Overall, Antarctica is an amazing example of the effect of globalization on the environmental web. Look at the contrast between the images of Antarctic exploration at the beginning of the 20th century (Figure 4.8) and those of tourists at an Antarctic base by the end of that century (Figure 6.17). The world has changed, and now anyone with sufficient money can visit Antarctica. Globalization has changed the continent from a remote and little known region supplying huge and unsustainable supplies of seals and whales, into a place that is considered a 'barometer' for the planet's health. One may deny that anthropogenic climate change is responsible for ice-shelf collapse, but who could deny the existence of the Antarctic ozone hole and its anthropogenic cause?

You have seen that the wealth of information and data available on the Internet is staggering, but it is often difficult to find the information you really need, and then determine how accurate it is. We hope that when faced with any question you can now gather information from the Internet and draw your own conclusions rather than just take it as read. If you want to know about the problems being discussed by the ATS or with CCAMLR why take an NGO's word for it when you can read their papers yourself? Combine this information with your knowledge of how ecosystems operate and you can identify problems yourself. Providing you have the background knowledge to tie it together, the possibilities are practically endless.

6.13 Summary of Chapter 6

6.1 Unsustainable exploitation of seal and whale populations in Antarctica in the early 20th century led to a steep decline in the numbers of these animals.

6.2 The Discovery Investigations research programme, set up to examine the impact of unsustainable exploitation, was instrumental in advancing our understanding of the Antarctic marine environment, ecosystem and ocean circulation.

6.3 The International Whaling Commission (IWC) was set up as an international attempt to manage the whaling industry. Despite whales numbers severely declining after World War II, it took until 1984 before a moratorium on whaling was implemented. In 2002 this moratorium was still in place.

6.4 Several countries made territorial claims in Antarctica before World War II, but the first permanent base in Antarctica was not established until 1944, by the British.

6.5 No nation could work out how to enforce sovereignty in Antarctica. With the American *Operation Highjump*, and the expansion of the FIDS, tension increased.

6.6 The International Geophysical Year of 1957–58 was the vehicle through which internationalization occurred. The result of this scientific event was the Antarctic Treaty System (ATS).

6.7 The Antarctic Treaty has 12 original signatories, although today the numbers have increased. Decisions on Antarctic matters south of 60° S are reached through the ATS by consensus.

6.8 The ATS has introduced four further pieces of legislation determining governance of Antarctica. The fourth — the Protocol on Environmental Protection to the Antarctic Treaty (1998) — was introduced because of the failure of a convention on mining (CRAMRA). This protocol now acts as a gatekeeper to Antarctica and means that an EIA must be prepared for all activities.

6.9 Antarctica is now a region of science and tourism. The resource exploitation is fishing activity, which is controlled by CCAMLR.

Once you have completed the Questions for Chapter 6, you should go to the Web and do the activities associated with this part of the chapter.

Learning Outcomes for Chapter 6

When you have completed this chapter you should be able to:

6.1 Define and use, or recognize definitions and applications of, each of the terms given in **bold** in the text. (Questions 6.1–6.3)

6.2 Describe facts about the exploitation and management of biological populations in Antarctica. (Questions 6.4, 6.5, 6.9, 6.10)

6.3 Describe facts about the history and development of Antarctic governance. (Questions 6.4, 6.6–6.9)

6.4 Describe facts about the history and relevance of scientific activity in Antarctica. (Questions 6.6, 6.7, 6.10)

6.5 Describe briefly the history of tourism in Antarctica and discuss how it may develop in future. (Question 6.11)

Questions for Chapter 6

Question 6.1

Explain what is meant by the ozone hole. Why is the ozone hole a problem?

Question 6.2

What is the difference between an Environmental Impact Assessment and a Comprehensive Environmental Evaluation?

Question 6.3

What is the difference between the Antarctic Treaty and the Antarctic Treaty System?

Question 6.4

Which of the following statements is *false*?

(a) Whale populations in Antarctica targeted by human hunters declined because the predation rate was greater than the whales' reproduction rates.

(b) The introduction of factory ships in the 1920s allowed a huge increase in the number of whales that could be caught in Antarctica because the whalers were no longer restricted to particular areas.

(c) Whalers had a large effect on terrestrial ecosystems in Antarctica as well as on marine ones.

(d) In the first half of the 20th century, the Norwegian Government controlled the whaling industry in Antarctica, and so collected large amounts of tax revenue from it.

(e) During the period when whales were hunted intensively, population numbers of larger whales fell first because these were the most profitable to catch.

(f) When larger whales became scarce, whalers shifted to hunting ever smaller whales.

Question 6.5

Which of the following could have helped to *increase* whale population numbers in the Antarctic, which would have tended to *decrease* them, and which would probably have had no effect?

(a) Whaling

(b) The setting up of the International Whaling Commission in 1946

(c) The moratorium on whaling declared by the IWC in 1982

(d) The decline of seal populations

(e) The lack of profit available from hunting when whale populations are very small

(f) The readmission of Iceland into the IWC

Question 6.6

Which two of the following statements are *false*?

(a) No one knows for certain who discovered Antarctica.

(b) The British Government claimed ownership of the Antarctic Peninsula from 20° W to 80° W in 1908.

(c) Britain, New Zealand and France were the first countries to make territorial claims in Antarctica.

(d) Captain James Cook made the first landing on South Georgia and claimed the island for Britain.

(e) Most territorial claims in Antarctica are based on geographical proximity or claims of first discovery.

(f) Territorial claims made before the Antarctic Treaty came into effect were recognized by international law as long as they were supported by human habitation.

(g) Most whalers on South Georgia were Norwegian.

(h) The Discovery Investigations established the continuous nature of the polar front around Antarctica, and included studies of the food, life history, and habits of whales and seals, the life cycle of krill, and the circulation of the Southern Ocean.

(i) The International Whaling Commission was set up to ensure the orderly development of the whaling industry.

(j) The USA used *Operation Highjump*, which placed nearly 5000 men in Antarctica, to reinforce its territorial claims.

(k) The first long-term research programme in Antarctica was set up by Argentina.

Question 6.7

Name the most important research initiative to take place in Antarctica (a) before 1950 and (b) after 1950. What was the significance of each initiative?

Question 6.8

Why could it be said that the following are limitations of the Antarctic Treaty System? Could it be argued that any of these are strengths?

(a) The articles of the Antarctic Treaty have been written in a deliberately imprecise way.

(b) Decisions can only be reached by consensus.

(c) The Antarctic Treaty covers the area south of 60° S.

Question 6.9

Which of the following statements is *false*?

(a) The Agreed Measures for the Conservation of Antarctic Fauna and Flora banned the importation of non-indigenous species to Antarctica.

(b) CCAMLR sets fishing quotas in the region south of the polar front.

(c) An ecosystem approach is used to set fishing quotas in Antarctica.

(d) The Greenpeace campaign in the 1980s was a major cause of the failure of CRAMRA.

(e) The introduction of the Protocol on Environmental Protection to the Antarctic Treaty led to a massive clean-up of Antarctica, banished huskies, and introduced EIAs and CEEs.

(f) The Protocol on Environmental Protection to the Antarctic Treaty finally resolved the debate on whether to allow mining for mineral resources that had been going on through the 1970s and 1980s by bringing in a permanent ban.

(g) The ecosystem approach sets a catch quota based on an understanding of all the ways that different animals in the whole ecosystem rely on the particular species that is to be harvested.

(h) Because the ecosystem approach takes account of all the factors affecting the numbers of a harvested species, a quota (TAC) can be set that is sustainable.

Question 6.10

List two major scientific discoveries in Antarctica since 1970 and briefly explain their relevance.

Question 6.11

Which of the following statements is *false*?

(a) There has been a decline in the numbers of penguins in a colony at Port Lockroy visited by tourists, compared with an undisturbed colony.

(b) Tourism in Antarctica began in the late 1950s.

(c) IAATO provides its passengers with guidelines for environmentally responsible tourism, that have been agreed by the Antarctic Treaty nations.

(d) Tourism in Antarctica has so far been successfully self-regulated.

(e) In 2005 there could be 20 000 visitors per year, compared with about 1000 per year in the 1970s.

References

Colonial Office, UK (1920) *Report of the Interdepartmental Committee on Research and Development in the Dependencies of the Falklands Islands*, Command paper No 657, 164 pp, London: HMSO.

CCAMLR (2001) Commission for the Conservation of Antarctic Marine Living Resources: Report of the twentieth meeting of the Commission, Hobart, Australia, 22 October–2 November 2001.

Fuchs, V. (1982) *Office and Men*. Oswestry: Anthony Nelson.

Hanson, J. D. and Gordon, J. E. (1998) *Antarctic Environments and Resources*. Harlow: Longman.

Hardy, A. (1967) *Great Waters*. London: Collins.

Headland, R. K. (1984) *The Island of South Georgia*. Cambridge: Cambridge University Press.

Hough, R. (1994) *Captain James Cook*. London: Hodder and Stoughton.

IWC (2002) [online] Available from: http://www.iwcoffice.org [Accessed November 2002]

Jackson, G. (1978) *The British Whaling Trade*. London: Adam and Charles Black.

May, J. (1988) *The Greenpeace Book of Antarctica*, London: Dorling Kindersley.

Lucas, C. E. and Cole, H. A.(1965) In Mackintosh, N. A. (1965) *The Stocks of Whales*. London: Fishing News.

Mickleburgh, E. (1987) *Beyond the Frozen Sea*. London: Paladin Books.

Siegert, M. J. (2001) Physical, chemical and biological processes in Lake Vostok and the Antarctic subglacial lakes. *Nature*, 2001, 603–609.

Sullivan, W., (1957) *Quest for a Continent*. London: Secker & Warburg.

Conclusion

Did it strike you as strange that people on coral atolls should be worrying about what is happening to the ice-shelves of Antarctica? Perhaps not. What may be even stranger is the fact that in today's world people on tropical islands and atolls worrying about Antarctica is starting to seem quite normal. This says a lot about just how globalized the world has become, and about the role of environmental issues in this globalization.

We have started this course not in your own backyard, nor even in the region or country in which you are likely to be living. In different ways, tropical islands and the continent of Antarctica are about as far from living in the northern temperate latitudes as you can get. For many centuries the existence of small oceanic islands and the great southern continent were the object of speculation and fantasy on the part of Europeans. Later, as they were pinned down into actual locations on the world map, they became places of scientific interest and armchair curiosity. Only in recent decades, however, has the fate of tropical islands and of the ice-covered southern continent taken on a direct and pressing relevance to ordinary people living thousands of miles away. In some senses, our attention is now held by Antarctica and islands like the Maldives as if they were our own backyard.

Today, there is a growing awareness that threats to biodiversity have a meaning and a significance far beyond the immediate location in which endangered species are to be found. To an even greater extent, global environmental changes, such as climate change and the thinning of the ozone layer, are giving rise to a new sense of connectedness to faraway places. While the human contribution to global changes may be of a scale without precedent, the point we have been making throughout this book is that distant regions across the globe have been linked for millions of years prior to any human impact. Indeed, it is the very existence of these ancient and ongoing patterns of teleconnection between regions and across the entire planet that transmits human impacts from one part of the globe to another.

In recent years, social scientists have noted that the tendency of environmental problems to spill over national boundaries is changing the way people think about countries and nations, leading us away from a sense of bounded and limited spaces to thinking about the world as a single interconnected place. This view has emerged from focusing predominantly on environmental issues like acid rain and leakage from nuclear power plants that have arisen over the past few decades in the most developed parts of the world. While the idea of environmental problems overflowing nation states is correct in some senses, it is also misleading, for it gives an impression that national boundaries came first, and environmental issues that overran them came later.

In this book we have taken a broader approach to environmental issues, looking deeper into the past and further afield. As our evidence implies, environmental problems predate the arrangement of countries or nations as they now stand. The division of the world into 'sovereign' states goes back at most a few hundred years, much less in some regions. But environmental disturbance recedes into a distant and prehistoric past. Wherever human beings have moved away from the ecosystems they are familiar with and into novel ecosystems, as we suggested, they have tended to take their old ways of viewing and doing things with them. The likely result has been environmental disturbance and following this disruption, a long and usually painful period of adjustment.

Over much of the world, the evidence of these periods of environmental change is buried beneath layers of physical and cultural change. But this is much less the case in those places that have been, until relatively recently, on the edge of the 'known world'. The last new lands and seas to be opened to human intervention provide some of the clearest and most dramatic records of rapid environmental change. The impact of settlement on small island ecosystems and the over-exploitation of the southern polar regions, as we have sought to demonstrate, brings into sharp relief the problem of environmental disturbance as an outcome of the lack of adjustment between human practices and ecosystems. But so do these cases offer some vital insights into the adjustment process: the business of learning and adapting to new ecosystems.

What we have also seen is that adjustment is not simply a process of learning to stay in the bounds of the ecosystem as it first appears. It means getting used to the natural variability of the system over time. The importance of this long-term learning is in many ways harder to glean from industrial societies. Because the industrial process is fuelled by non-renewable energy sources and raw materials that are usually sourced from far afield it is much more difficult to gauge when the systems that are relied upon are being placed under pressure and rendered vulnerable.

What we now have to consider is that the loss of resilience in ecosystems — which we have observed in 'peripheral' cases like small islands and the Southern Ocean ecosystem — might now apply on a much larger scale. As industrial production, including industrialized agriculture, makes ever greater inroads into ecosystems across the planet, the issue of decreased resilience may now be presenting itself at a global level. Our understanding of ENSO and other major climatic oscillations, together with our growing knowledge of major catastrophic shifts like the periodic break-up of the West Antarctic Ice-Sheet suggests that disruptions on a major scale are part of the normal workings of our planet — if it is viewed in the long term. This is the case, even without the human contribution to major geoclimatic change.

What we need to recognize is that intensifying human activity is increasing the likelihood of major disturbances at the same time that it is undermining the resilience of ecosystems across the planet. In this sense, it is not just the disasters of small islands or the Southern Ocean ecosystem that we have to keep in mind. It is also the responses to these events, and what we might learn from them. In particular, the way that Antarctica and the ocean around it is being viewed as a kind of shared space — or 'commons' for the globe might have implications on a far larger scale. Though the outcomes are far from perfect or complete, the processes of governance that have emerged out of disputes over the southern polar regions and others may turn out to have had much broader implications for governing the planet as a whole.

While conflicts and negotiations over Antarctica and its seas began as a contest between colonial powers, we have seen that non-governmental organizations such as Greenpeace — which combine expert knowledge with broad-based popular support — have been able to exert an important influence. We have also seen that islands such as the Maldives have taken a stand on the global stage over global environmental changes that affect them. In the last three chapters you gained further insights into the ways that new electronic media allow us to gain direct access to data that ~~can~~ we can use and manipulate to come to our own conclusions and develop our own arguments. These are all vital steps on the way to a broadened participation in governance — not only at a local level but reaching out to encompass events of global significance.

Answers to Questions

Chapter 1

Question 1.1

(b), (c) and (e) are misleadingly one-sided in their reading of globalization. (a) and (d) give a more useful impression of the 'ambivalence' of globalization.

Question 1.2

Your answer should be along the following lines. Increasing numbers of tourists require more facilities and services, which runs the risk of undermining the very scenic and environmental attractions that draw tourists to small islands. Unrestrained tourist development also places increasing demands on the environmental resources of a small island, which are not likely to be sustainable. You might also have mentioned the cultural impacts of tourism.

Question 1.3

(a) and (d). Sustainable development is intended to bridge the gap between developed and less-developed countries, without long-term damage to the environment, and without curtailing the growth of the already developed societies.

Question 1.4

Someone living in the British Isles is quite likely to be attracted to the idea of slightly warmer temperatures, and everything this implies for life-style. A Maldivian who is aware of the link between warming and sea-level rise is more likely to take a dim view of even a slight change. You might also consider, however, that your British Islander may be aware of the threat that sea-level change holds to low-lying parts of the British Isles, and that both of your 'respondents' might have a 'global' awareness of the impact of warming on people elsewhere.

Question 1.5

Obvious answers include coastal erosion, and the salt-water contamination of freshwater aquifers. Another possible answer is that rising sea-levels also worsen the effects of storms — especially when storm surges take place.

Question 1.6

Your answer should include the following points: ten years is too short a time period to capture long-term trends; one island is not a large enough sample to represent an entire region, and certainly cannot represent the whole planet. Furthermore, because climate varies naturally, the demonstration of a warming trend does not necessarily point to human impact.

Question 1.7

All of the listed points, apart from (f), could account for an observed increase in sea-level. (f) would be likely to give the impression of falling sea-levels.

Question 1.8

The three main factors are volcanic activity, the upheaval caused by continental plates colliding or riding up over each other, and the accretion of coral — from the bodies of small marine organisms. You might also have mentioned that decreasing sea-level can bring a previously sunken land formation into full view. (You may also have heard of islands built up out of accumulated bird excrement or 'guano'.)

Question 1.9

(b), (c) and (e) each suggest a misunderstanding of uncertainty. (b) ignores the fact that some forms of uncertainty are an inevitable consequence of the way some systems work in the physical world. (c) overlooks the fact that the physical world can give rise to genuine novelty, which inevitably involves uncertainty. (e) fails to consider the potential for decision-makers to account for uncertainty by building it into the decision-making process.

Question 1.10

(a) and (e) are true. (b) takes the term 'catastrophe' too literally, and ignores the fact that catastrophic changes take place all around us at many scales — without necessarily having undesirable effects. (c) is incorrect because changes tend to be sudden, with few visible signs that they are imminent. (d) misses the point that systems of this kind tend to be attracted to one state or the other — with the intermediate positions being highly unstable and transient.

Chapter 2

Question 2.1

(a) and (c) are correct. (b) is incorrect because smaller ecosystems, such as ponds or creeks, are part of larger ecosystems such as wetlands or river systems, which implies that an organism can be part of ecosystems at several different scales. (d) is incorrect because both organic and inorganic matter is exchanged with surrounding systems. (e) is incorrect because human beings are part of the ecosystems they dwell in, and because social systems interface with ecosystems in many ways.

Question 2.2

(a) Fresh food; (b) fresh water; (c) timber, for ship repairs, etc; (d) a place for rest and recuperation; (e) an island was also a meeting place where different crews could exchange information and commodities.

Question 2.3

Deforestation left soil exposed, resulting in erosion. Eroded soil silted up rivers and harbours and contaminated fresh water supplies. It was widely conjectured (correctly) that deforestation could alter local climates ('microclimates'). There was some understanding of the role of forests in forming mist and precipitating rain, so deforestation was linked to declining rainfall.

Question 2.4

(a) Its behaviour was 'naive' (that is, it lacked the experience of predators that would have made it more cautious and defensive).

(b) It was flightless.

(c) It was ground-nesting.

(d) Its reproduction rate was relatively slow (only one egg per clutch).

Question 2.5

Governance encompasses all the many ways in which people influence the steering and management of their societies. It includes the processes by which ordinary people at the 'bottom' or 'grassroots' level of their societies make contributions, as well as the procedures undertaken by people in positions of greater power. Government implies the directing and managing of society from 'above', usually by small groups who specialize in decision-making and the wielding of power.

Question 2.6

The correct historical sequence is (c), (b), (f), (e), (d), (a).

Question 2.7

(a), (c) and (d) are correct. (b) is incorrect, because the particular cluster of genes which a founder population brings with it to an island does not necessarily prepare it for the new environment. (e) is incorrect because the genetic range of the founder population is only the starting point for the new phase of evolutionary development. Subsequently, selection pressures play a major role.

Question 2.8

Human factors such as overexploitation of species, habitat destruction and bioinvasion all weaken the resilience of a species, though the species may survive immediate human impact. At some later stage, perhaps through several episodes, natural extremes or variability, such as drought or cyclone, may provide the stress that the species population cannot survive — resulting in extinction.

Question 2.9

While species introduced by Polynesians may have come via other islands, some of these species were originally from the mainland (e.g. rats, pigs, dogs), and were therefore quite alien to oceanic islands. Their introduction is likely to have led to severe degradation of ecosystems in many cases. Some species brought in from neighbouring islands may well have fitted into island ecosystems without major stress. However, we should keep in mind that island species have often diverged markedly, even from their relatives on neighbouring islands, so the risks of relocation may also be high. In general, however, organisms transplanted from within the vicinity of the new island are likely to have coevolved more easily with island ecosystems than organisms from further away.

Question 2.10

(c) and (d) are correct. (a) is incorrect because it does not allow for coevolution between humans and other components of ecosystems over time. (b) is incorrect because it over-rates the potential of culture and social organization, ignoring the fact that social and cultural factors can inhibit as well as assist coevolution.

Chapter 3

Question 3.1

(a), (b) and (e) are correct. (c) is incorrect because of the claim that complex systems have no external connections. (d) is incorrect because not all feedback loops serve to stabilize the system. Moreover, many simple systems are very stable.

Question 3.2

This is an unwise strategy. This is because the change from a reef dominated by coral to one dominated by macroalgae tends to be catastrophic rather than gradual. What this means is that there are likely to be few visible signs that conditions are building up to shift. By the time there is clear visible evidence of a takeover by macroalgae it would probably be too late to reverse tourist development trends and prevent the shift taking place.

Question 3.3

(c) and (d) are valid reasons. (a) and (b) are incorrect because computer modelling can give us very useful information about the real world, including the modelling of feedbacks, if we take into account its limitations. (e) is incorrect, because catastrophic shifts are not random, and it is, at least hypothetically, possible to predict them.

Question 3.4

(a) and (d) are the correct answers. (b) is incorrect because it is impossible to prevent all disturbance and because all ecosystems have evolved to cope with certain levels of disturbance. (c) is incorrect, because loss of redundancy increases the vulnerability to present and future disturbances.

Question 3.5

(a), (c) and (d) are correct. (b) is incorrect, as agricultural production involves many more reductions or simplifications of the ecosystem than it does additions.

Question 3.6

(a) and (d) are correct. (b) is incorrect because the factors causing or 'forcing' ENSO are distinct from those which influence the monsoon. (c) is misleading, because it now seems that ENSO only has a major influence on the monsoon during phase-locking. (e) is incorrect, as phase-locking exacerbates the effects of the two systems, rather than cancelling them out.

Question 3.7

(b), (d) and (f) are correct. (a) is incorrect as market forces are most likely to make food available to those who can pay for it, that is, the least needy. (c) is incorrect as maximizing land-use reduces redundancy in the system. (e) is incorrect as the most needy are unlikely to have the economic resources to meet tax increases.

Question 3.8

Extreme rain deficit is likely to cause serious crop failure or reduction. Economic downturn will reduce the revenue earned from those crops that do make it on to the global market. These effects are likely to reinforce each other, making it extremely difficult for a farmer to recover from adversity.

Question 3.9

(b), (c) and (d) are all top-down. It is important to recognize that top-down governance is not necessarily harmful. In the case of (c) — redistribution of food between regions — it may only be state or provincial governors who have the capacity for this kind of response to adverse conditions. (a) is incorrect because it suggests a much more local, bottom-up form of decision-making, although village-level decision-making is not necessarily democratic or all-inclusive. (e) and (f) are both incorrect as they involve decisions at the local or individual level, including the decision to participate in a global market where it is freely taken and not enforced from above.

Question 3.10

The great differences in power and wealth between people who are drawn into global markets suggest an uneven 'playing field'. Climatic differences and other forms of environmental variability can also be viewed as a kind of unevenness.

Chapter 4

Question 4.1

The main feature of the coreless winter is that there is no definable minimum winter temperature. From summer to autumn temperature falls rapidly, and then stays within a narrow range until spring. We do not see the coreless winter on the coast of Antarctica because of the close proximity of the ocean.

Question 4.2

An ice-shelf is glacial ice that remains attached to the land but is floating on the ocean. This means that the ice displaces the same weight of water as it contains. As it melts, water is not added to the ocean and so sea-level remains constant. (You can do this experiment yourself with a glass of water and some ice.)

Question 4.3

We cannot be sure. There are several competing claims, for example William Smith landed on King George Island in 1819, a British ship sighted and charted the Trinity Peninsula in 1820, and American and Russian ships also sighted the mainland at about the same time. In reality, Antarctica was almost certainly discovered by an unnamed sealing ship.

Question 4.4

In a Mercator projection lines of latitude are horizontal, and lines of longitude are vertical. If we draw the whole of Antarctica using this system, the region is very distorted and it is very hard to see the shape of the land. The South Pole cannot be represented as a point but only as the whole of the 180° S line of latitude. A polar projection is much more useful.

Question 4.5

(d) The United States have not made a territorial claim in Antarctica.

Question 4.6

Antarctica is fringed by ice-shelves that are continually calving icebergs. This means that as each iceberg drifts away from Antarctica, it reduces the area of the continent slightly. This change can be more drastic when an entire ice-shelf collapses.

Question 4.7

Antarctica was located at a southern latitude similar to that of Australia today. This means that we should expect it to have had a similar climate and be mostly ice-free.

Question 4.8

No. The United Kingdom is in the Northern Hemisphere and Antarctica is in the Southern. This means that the warmest temperatures will be when the United Kingdom is suffering its winter.

Question 4.9

Glacial ice is formed from snow and so is made of freshwater.

Question 4.10

The ease of finding information on the Internet makes it very tempting to use the first information that you find. It is important to try and get some idea of how ‘good’ your first source is.

Question 4.11

By carefully specifying requirements for information one can be more specific about the information one requires.

Chapter 5

Question 5.1

The polar front acts as a barrier in the Southern Ocean with warmer water to the north. The island to the south will be surrounded by this cold water and its temperature will be reduced. The cold temperatures mean that precipitation can fall as snow and glaciers could grow. The island to the north of the polar front will be much warmer and any precipitation will fall as rain.

Question 5.2

The levels are:

(a) killer whale: top carnivore

(b) penguin, (f) crabeater seal and (d) baleen whale: carnivores

(c) krill: mainly herbivores

(e) phytoplankton: primary producer

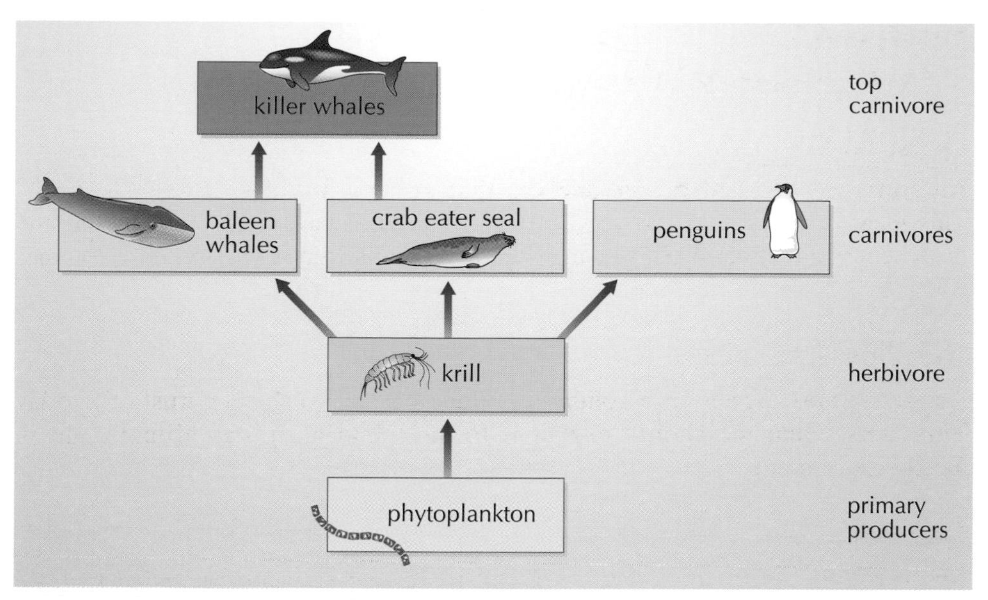

Figure A1 An example of a simplified food chain.

Humans would appear towards the top of the food chain in a carnivore trophic level.

Question 5.3

Primary producers become entrained in the ice when the frazil ice develops into pancake ice and traps seawater in the ice matrix. This would happen when the ice is advancing, i.e. in the southern autumn and winter. From Figure 5.3 this would be generally from March–June.

Question 5.4

The raw materials for phytoplankton growth are not uniformly distributed around Antarctica, so phytoplankton growth is patchy. This means that as the frazil ice forms pancake ice, only those regions rich in phytoplankton will entrain a layer of chlorophyll.

Question 5.5

As sea-ice is made of frozen seawater, when it retreats it will not affect sea-level. The snow that is on top of the sea-ice will contribute to a higher sea-level, but this is not significant.

Question 5.6

The blue whale can survive on krill for two reasons. The first is that there is a short food chain from primary producer to predator and so a significant amount of energy is transferred. Second, the krill exhibit swarming behaviour which concentrates many individuals in a small area. As a result, the whale can ingest many of them at once.

Question 5.7

Iron is thought to be the missing raw material that holds back biological production in large parts of the Southern Ocean. If iron could be added to the waters here, then the theory is that primary producers could be stimulated into growth. As they grow CO_2 would be used and possibly sucked from the atmosphere into the ocean. This could reduce or even stop the increase of atmospheric CO_2, and so mitigate climate change.

Chapter 6

Question 6.1

The ozone hole is an area of low atmospheric ozone concentration in the stratosphere, centred over Antarctica. It is a problem because ozone absorbs ultraviolet light, which, if it reaches the surface of the Earth, can damage living cells.

Question 6.2

An EIA must be carried out for any planned activity in Antarctica to assess the effects on the environment of that activity. A CEE is also carried out to assess the effects of an activity on the environment but only if those effects are considered to be anything more than minor.

Question 6.3

The Antarctic Treaty is an international agreement, signed in 1958, which came into effect in 1961. Under the treaty, all new decisions about global policy south of 60° S must be made by unanimous agreement. The Antarctic Treaty System includes not only the Antarctic Treaty, but four further international agreements: Agreed Measures for the Conservation of Antarctic Fauna and Flora (1964); Convention for the Conservation of Antarctic Seals (1972); Convention for the Conservation of Antarctic Marine Living Resources (1982); and Protocol of Environmental Protection to the Antarctic Treaty (1998). CCAMLR controls the exploitation of the Antarctic marine environment south of the Antarctic Convergence — i.e. a much larger area than the original Antarctic Treaty, which only covers the area south of 60° S.

Question 6.4

(d) is false, because the British Government controlled most of the whaling in the Southern Ocean and collected revenues from the whalers, though most of the whalers were Norwegian.

Question 6.5

(a) Whaling, by increasing the predation rate on whales, would tend to decrease population numbers.

(b) The setting up of the International Whaling Commission in 1946, in itself, would have had no effect on whale numbers.

(c) The moratorium on whaling declared by the IWC in 1982 would have helped to increase whale numbers by reducing the predation rate.

(d) The decline of seal populations could have helped to increase whale numbers because the competition between whales and seals for food would be decreased.

(e) The lack of profit available from hunting when whale populations are very small would have helped to increase whale numbers because whaling stopped as a result of the low profits, thereby reducing the predation rate on whales.

(f) The readmission of Iceland into the IWC might be enough to swing the vote in favour of a resumption of whaling and, if this happened, whale numbers are likely to decrease.

Question 6.6

(f) and (k) are false. No territorial claims in Antarctica are recognized under international law and the first long-term research programme in Antarctica was set up by Britain (the Discovery Investigations).

Question 6.7

The Discovery Investigations took place in the 1920s. It was the first major research initiative in Antarctica and was very ambitious in its aims. The International Geophysical Year took place in 1957–1958. It was an international collaboration, with 67 countries involved, which resulted in a massive increase in scientific effort in the region and left a legacy in the form of a proliferation of Antarctic bases.

Question 6.8

The limitations are that imprecise articles create problems with interpretation, reaching consensus can take a long time, and the area south of 60° S does not include the whole Antarctic ecosystem (which includes all the area as far north as the polar front). It could be argued that (a) and (b) are strengths because the imprecise wording of Article IV puts all territorial disputes into abeyance for an indefinite time, and because every member of the ATS has equal voting rights regardless of how much money they put into Antarctic research.

Question 6.9

(f) is false. The Protocol on Environmental Protection to the Antarctic Treaty did resolve the debate on whether to allow mining for mineral resources in Antarctica but only temporarily, by banning it for 50 years.

Question 6.10

The discovery in 1985 by the British Antarctic Survey of the ozone hole, caused by the release to the atmosphere of synthetic chemicals such as CFCs, now controlled through the introduction of global legislation.

The discovery in the 1970s of Lake Vostok and other freshwater lakes below the Antarctic ice-cap. The water in Lake Vostok has been out of contact with the atmosphere for over 500 000 years, and it could contain unique life forms. It could also present similar conditions to those found on Europa, the moon of Jupiter, which would make it a useful model for NASA, or any other agency planning to journey to Europa.

Question 6.11

(a) is false. A scientific study of a penguin colony at Port Lockroy, which is visited very frequently by tourists, revealed no effects on the penguins compared with an undisturbed colony.

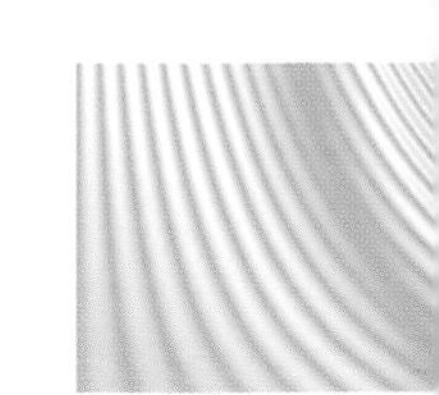

Acknowledgements

Grateful acknowledgement is made to the following sources for permission to reproduce material in this book:

Chapter 1

Figure1.1a: Getmapping; *Figure 1.1b*: Courtesy of Professor Bob Spicer; *Figure 1.2*: Bantam Press, a division of Transworld Publishers Ltd, 1990/Bantam Books, a division of Bantam Doubleday Dell Publishing Group, Inc., 1990, © John and Mary Gribbin, 1990, and by permission of Murray Pollinger; *Figures 1.3, 1.4, 1.6, 1.10*: Courtesy of Marion Hall; *Figure 1.5*: Courtesy of Professor Bob Spicer; *Figure 1.7*: Andy Crump/Still Pictures; *Figure 1.8*: Image State/Pictor; *Figure 1.9*: Crown copyright material reproduced under Class Licence Number C01W0000065 with the permission of the Controller of HMSO and the Queen's Printer for Scotland; *Figure 1.11*: Courtesy of Mark Brandon; *Figure 1.14*: Photographer Lloyd Homer, copyright, Institute of Geological and Nuclear Sciences Ltd.

Chapter 2

Figure 2.1: Courtesy of Marion Hall; *Figure 2.2*: © Kim Crosbie; *Figure 2.4*: © The Natural History Museum, London; *Figure 2.5*: © Shelburne Museum, Shelburne, Vermont; *Figure 2.7*: Courtesy of Mark Brandon; *Figure 2.8*: Pyne, S. J. (1997) *Vestal Fire: An Environmental History, Told through Fire, of Europe and Europe's Encounter with the World*, University of Washington Press; *Figure 2.9*: The canoe of Tchani's Family by Herb Kawainui Kane; *Figure 2.10*: Courtesy of Pro Chile.

Chapter 3

Figure 3.1: Florida Keys National Marine Sanctuary Staff; *Figures 3.2, 3.7, 3.8a, 3.8b, 3.10b, 3.15a, 3.15b*: Courtesy of Marion Hall; *Figure 3.3*: International Stock/Robert Harding; *Figure 3.4*: Ursula Keuper-Bennett/Peter Bennett TURTLE TRAX; *Figure 3.6*: National Oceanic and Atmospheric Administration/Department of Commerce; *Figures 3.9, 3.11*: Davis, M. (2001) *Late Victorian Holocausts*, Verso; *Figure 3.10a*: Darius Klemens/Link; *Figure 3.13*: Ilay Cooper/Images of India/Link; *Figure 3.14*: Los Angeles County Museum of Art, Purchased with funds provided by Christian Humann. Photograph © 2003 Museum Associates/LACMA.

Chapter 4

Figures 4.1, 4.17, 4.18: Courtesy of Mark Brandon; *Figure 4.3*: Royal Geographic Society; *Figure 4.4*: Centre for Astrophysical Research in Antarctica, University of Chicago Department of Astronomy and Astrophysics; *Figure 4.6*: MODIS image courtesy of NASA's Terra satellite, supplied by Ted Scambos, National Snow an Ice Data Center, University of Colorado, Boulder; *Figure 4.8*: British Museum; *Figure 4.9*: Bryan and Cherry Alexander Photography; *Figure 4.10*: Walton, D. W. H. (ed.) (1987) *Antarctic Science*, Cambridge University Press; *Figure 4.13*: Science Museum/ Science and Society Picture Library; *Figure 4.14*: Dietz, R. S. and Holden, J. C. (1970) *Journal of Geophysical Research*, **75** © 1970 American Geophysical Union; *Figures 4.15, 4.16*: © Richard Hodgkins.

Chapter 5

Figures 5.1 and 5.2: National Oceanic and Atmospheric Administration; *Figure 5.3*: Zwally, H. Jay et al. (2002), Variability of Antarctic sea ice 1979–1998, **107**, C5, *Journal of Geophysical Research* Copyright © American Geophysical Union; *Figures 5.4, 5.11, 5.14, 5.15*: Courtesy of Mark Brandon; *Figure 5.5*: © Dr Kevin Hughes; *Figure 5.6a*: Steve Turner/OSF; *Figure 5.6b*: © Kim Crosbie; *Figures 5.7a, 5.12*: © Julian Priddle; *Figure 5.7b*: NASA; *Figure 5.9*: British Antarctic Survey; *Figure 5.10*: Tynan, C. T. (1998) Ecological importance of the Southern Boundary of the Antarctic Circumpolar Current, *Nature*, **392**, 16 April 1998, © Macmillan Magazines Ltd.

Chapter 6

Tables

Table 6.1 International Whaling Committee.

Figures

Figure 6.1: Scott Polar Research Institute, University of Cambridge; *Figures 6.2, 6.5, 6.7b, 6.15, 6.16, 6.17*: Courtesy of Mark Brandon; *Figures 6.3, 6.4*: © Sir Alister Hardy; *Figures 6.6, 6.9*: © Walter Sullivan; *Figure 6.7a*: © ADAGP, Paris and DACS, London 2003; *Figure 6.10* © National Academy of Sciences; *Figure 6.13*: © 1988 Greenpeace Communications Limited; *Figure 6.14*: NASA.

Every effort has been made to trace all the copyright owners, but if any has been inadvertently overlooked, the publishers will be pleased to make the necessary arrangements at the first opportunity.

Index

Entries in **bold** are key terms. Page numbers referring to information that is given only in a figure or caption are printed in *italics*.

D

E

F